Drinkers of Infinity
Essays 1955–1967

Books by Arthur Koestler

Novels
THE GLADIATORS*
DARKNESS AT NOON
ARRIVAL AND DEPARTURE*
THIEVES IN THE NIGHT*
THE AGE OF LONGING

Autobiography
DIALOGUE WITH DEATH*
SCUM OF THE EARTH*
ARROW IN THE BLUE
THE INVISIBLE WRITING
THE GOD THAT FAILED (with others)

Essays
THE YOGI AND THE COMMISSAR*
INSIGHT AND OUTLOOK
PROMISE AND FULFILMENT
THE TRAIL OF THE DINOSAUR
REFLECTIONS ON HANGING
THE SLEEPWALKERS*
THE LOTUS AND THE ROBOT*
THE ACT OF CREATION
THE GHOST IN THE MACHINE
SUICIDE OF A NATION? (edit)

Theatre
TWILIGHT BAR

* Available in the Danube Edition

ARTHUR KOESTLER

Drinkers of Infinity
Essays 1955–1967

THE MACMILLAN COMPANY

Library of Congress Catalog Card Number: 74-75395

First American Edition 1969

First published in Great Britain in 1968 by Hutchinson & Co. (Publishers) Ltd., London

The Macmillan Company

Printed in the United States of America

TO SIR CYRIL BURT,
in gratitude for what he taught us

Contents

Preface

Some of these essays were written for magazines and broad-
casting; others are papers addressed to such varied audiences
as the British Association for the Advancement of Science
and the Royal Society of Literature, the Brain Research
Institute of the University of California and the Festival of
Vienna. But although they differ in style and weight, they
could be called variations on certain themes. The themes
are by and large those of the books I wrote in the twelve-year
period covered by this collection. Several of these books are
rather long, deal with complex subjects and include a certain
amount of technical detail. In each of the essays, on the
other hand, I have picked a single thread out of the tangled
web, where it could not be easily discerned. Thus each essay
in the section 'Gravity and the Holy Ghost' singles out a
different leitmotif from *The Sleepwalkers* or *The Act of Creation*.
Similarly, the essays in the section 'The Horse in the Locomotive' are—as the title indicates—variations on certain themes
in *The Ghost in the Machine*. The selection of 'Books Reviewed',
too, is meant to show a certain thematic coherence.

Here and there, the attentive reader may find that a
sentence or paragraph has a familiar ring. This is either
because I wrote the essay in question before the book to
which it is related, and then incorporated parts of the essay

into the book; or conversely, I may have paraphrased or quoted a passage from a book in these essays, without giving chapter and verse, which is always a bore where one's own work is concerned.

The section on 'The Lion and the Ostrich' is related to two other books: *Reflections on Hanging* and *Suicide of a Nation?* The former was written for the Campaign for the Abolition of Capital Punishment, in which I took an active part (and which was actually initiated by the late Sir Victor Gollancz, Canon John Collins and myself). At the height of the Campaign, when *The Observer* was serialising that controversial book, I also wrote articles on the purely legal aspects of murder trials under the non-controversial pseudonym *Vigil*. The article on 'The Unreasonable Murderer' is included as a sample of that judicious worthy's reports on the murderous subtleties of Common Law.

The two articles on 'Animals in Quarantine' in the same section relate to a relatively minor scandal which, however, has gone on virtually unchallenged for half a century in this land of dog-lovers. They, too, brought in their wake a grotesquely emotional controversy; petitions were organised and campaign committees formed, but in this case without any result—apart from conferring on the author the proud title of a Vice-President of the National Dog Owners' Association.

The last piece in this section, and 'Europe, My Europe!' require no particular comment; except perhaps that I have included in the latter a couple of escapist travelogues; and why not?

Although some of the papers were addressed to scientific conferences or learned institutions, I have edited out technical details. With the possible exception of one item (to name it would have a putting-off effect) this volume should present no difficulty to the general reader.

A.K.

London
January, 1968

Gravity and the Holy Ghost

Gravity and the Holy Ghost

*Lecture delivered at the Symposium on 'The Scientific and
Artistic Achievements of the Century of Enlightenment' at the
Cini Foundation, Venice, September 1967.*

When Newton died in 1727, Alexander Pope, the most
fashionable poet at that time, wrote this oft-quoted epitaph:

> Nature and Nature's Laws lay hid in night:
> God said let Newton be, and all was light.

Pope certainly voiced the mood of the Age of Reason, of
that Pan-European New Philosophy which was emerging out
of the Scientific Revolution of the previous century, and
whose cornerstone was the Newtonian cosmology. It was
this new view of the universe which lent the whole movement
its characteristic mixture of humility and arrogance. The
humility came from the realisation that our earth is not the
centre of the world and that humanity is reduced to the condition of 'so many ants crawling on a flying balloon'. This
metaphor, devised by one of Galileo's critics,* with intent to
ridicule, had now become sober reality. But there was arrogance to compensate for man's hurt pride. The tiny ants had
huge brains which, aided by the polished lenses of the telescope, enabled them to encompass all infinity. John Donne

* Monsignor Querengo.

3

was quick in perceiving this note of *hubris* in Galileo's report on his astronomic discoveries:

> Man has weaved out a net and this net thrown
> Upon the heavens and now they are his own.

The Newtonian edifice provided the framework for the philosophy of the Age of Enlightenment. Once that edifice was completed, it looked like an entirely rational construction. But it was not built by rational, logical steps. One of its chief architects was a German mystic, Johannes Kepler. The tortuous road by which he arrived at his famous three laws of planetary motion—the cornerstones of modern astronomy —is characteristic of the great convulsions and confusions of thought during the transition from the mediaeval to the scientific world-view. I shall try briefly to retrace his development, because it forms a little-known, but symbolic prologue to the *secolo dei lumi*—its birth-pangs, as it were.

'If I could see further than others,' Newton once remarked, 'it was because I stood on the shoulders of giants.' The principal giants were of course Copernicus, Galileo and Kepler.

Canon Copernick had died in 1543 at the age of seventy: the first printed copy of his book *On the Revolutions of the Heavenly Spheres* was handed to him on his deathbed. Its first thirty pages outlined the theory of the heliocentric universe; the rest of the book, describing the motions of the earth, moon and planets, is so confusing and unreadable that it became an all-time worst-seller. There are indications that even Galileo did not read all through it. Its first edition of a thousand copies never sold out, and it had altogether four reprints in four hundred years. A contemporary astronomical work, Christoph Clavius' *The Treatise on the Sphere*, had nineteen reprints within fifty years—Copernicus' book one.

I mention this curiosity to show that the Copernican theory attracted very little attention in Europe for the next two generations. It was not put on the Index of the Holy Office until 1616 that is, seventy-three years after its publication (and then only for four years, 'pending corrections'). New ideas, like infectious diseases, need a period of incubation before their full impact makes itself felt. Kepler was the first astronomer to raise his voice in public in favour of the Copernican theory. His *Mysterium Cosmographicum*, published in 1597—fifty-four years after Copernicus' death—initiated the controversy. Galileo entered the scene fifteen years later.

Kepler was twenty-five when he wrote the *Mysterium*, and at that time he knew very little of astronomy. He had started as a hopeful student of theology at the Lutheran University of Tübingen, but a chance opportunity brought him as a teacher of mathematics to the provincial school of Gratz in Austria. In an autobiographical sketch which he also wrote at twenty-five, he described the varied interests of his student-years; they ranged from the writing of comedies and Pindaric odes, to compositions 'on unusual subjects, such as the resting place of the sun, and the sources of rivers, the sight of Atlantis through the clouds, the heavens, the spirits, the genii, the nature of fire, and other things of the same kind'. In this varied menu of preoccupations one also finds the following remark: 'I often defended the opinions of Copernicus in the disputations of the students, and I composed a careful disputation on the first motion which consists in the rotation of the earth [around its axis]; then I added to this the motion of the earth around the sun *for physical, or if you prefer, metaphysical reasons.*'

I have emphasised the last phrase because it can be found verbatim repeated in various passages in his works, and contains the leitmotif of his quest—which was eventually to lead him to the laws of planetary motion, and provide the mathematical foundations of the Newtonian universe.

Kepler became acquainted with Copernicus' book through one of his teachers in Tübingen, a certain Michael Maestlin, who possessed a copy of it—although Maestlin himself, like everybody else (including Galileo) taught the traditional, earth-centred Ptolemaic astronomy. Six years later, in the Preface to the *Mysterium Cosmographicum*, Kepler wrote:

5

> I was so delighted with Copernicus . . . that I proceeded to ascribe to the earth the apparent motions of the sun *for physical, or if you like it better, for metaphysical reasons*—as Copernicus had done for mathematical reasons.

He then proceeded to explain his metaphysical reasons for preferring a heliocentric to a geocentric world. Surprising though it may seem, they were based on a supposed analogy between the stationary sun, the stars and interstellar space on the one hand, and God the Father, the Son and the Holy Ghost on the other. 'I shall pursue this analogy in my future cosmographical work,' he promised. And twenty-five years later, when he was over fifty, he reaffirmed his belief in it: 'It is by no means permissible to treat this analogy as an empty comparison; it must be considered by its Platonic form and archetypal quality as one of the primary causes.'

He believed in this to the end of his life; it was one of the axioms of faith on which his edifice was built. But gradually his cherished analogy underwent a significant change. In a letter to Maestlin of the period in which the *Mysterium Cosmographicum* was written, he explained:

> The sun in the middle of the moving stars, himself at rest and yet the source of motion, carries the image of God the Father and Creator. He distributes his motive force through a medium which contains the moving bodies, even as the Father creates through the Holy Ghost.

It should be noted that at this point the 'moving bodies', that is, the planets, are brought into the picture. The sun has become their 'source of motion'; the Holy Ghost no longer merely fills the space between the motionless sun and the motionless stars: it has now become an active agent, a *vis motrix*, which drives the nimble planets in their orbits. Nobody before had suspected the existence of such a force emanating from the sun—except perhaps the Pythagoreans. But for the last two thousand years astronomy had been concerned not with the causes of the heavenly motions but with their description in purely geometrical terms, divorced from all physical considerations.

6

I would like to suggest that the passages I have just quoted reflect the first hesitant introduction of physical causation into man's vision of the skies—the first intimation of the forthcoming synthesis of cosmography and physics. I shall return to this point in a moment; but first let us follow the gradual transformation of the Holy Ghost into a physical force.

In the twentieth chapter of the *Mysterium*, Kepler attacks the problem of the mathematical relation between a planet's distance from the sun and the speed of its motion. This again was a question which nobody before him had raised, because it implied a causal connection of a physical nature between the sun and the planets—and such an idea, as I said, was completely strange to mediaeval cosmology. Now, the greater their distance from the sun, the slower the planets move (both regarding angular and tangential velocity). This phenomenon, says Kepler, allows only the following two explanations:

> Either the souls (*animae*) which move the planets are the less active the farther the planet is removed from the sun, or there exists only *one moving soul in the centre of all the orbits*, that is, the sun, which drives the planet the more vigorously the closer the planet is, but whose force is quasi-exhausted when acting on the outer planets because of the long distance and the weakening of the force which it entails.

Twenty-five years later, commenting on this passage, he wrote:

> If we substitute for the word 'soul' the word 'force' then we get just the principle which underlies my physics of the skies in the *Astronomia Nova* . . . Once I firmly believed that the motive force of a planet was a soul . . . Yet as I reflected that this cause of motion diminishes in proportion to distance, just as the light of the sun diminishes in proportion to distance from the sun, I came to the conclusion that this force must be something substantial—'substantial' not in the literal sense but . . . in the same manner as we say that light is something substantial, meaning by this an unsubstantial entity emanating from a substantial body.

7

The twenty-five years that separate these two quotations mark the transition from *anima motrix* to *vis motrix*, from a universe animated by purposeful intelligences to one moved by inanimate, 'blind' forces devoid of purpose. For the rest of his life Kepler struggled with this new concept of 'force' emerging from the womb of animism (its very name, *virtus*, or *vis*, betrays its origin) without ever coming to terms with it. At first he was not aware of the difficulties inherent in it. While he was working on his *magnum opus*, the *Astronomia Nova*, he wrote with youthful optimism to a friend:

> My aim is to show that the heavenly machine is not a kind of divine, live being, but a kind of clockwork (and he who believes that a clock has a soul, attributes the maker's glory to the work), in so far as nearly all the manifold motions are caused by a most simple, magnetic, and material force, just as all motions of the clock are caused by a simple weight. And I also show how these physical causes are to be given numerical and geometrical expression.

Kepler had defined the essence of the Scientific Revolution. But it turned out to be easier to talk about a 'most simple, magnetic, material force' than to form a concrete idea of its working. Kepler's efforts to visualise the nature of the 'moving force' emanating from the sun are not only of interest from the historian's point of view; they also illuminate the philosophical difficulties that were inherent in the concept of force from its very beginning. Since no English, French or Italian translation of the *Astronomia Nova* exists as far as I know, a few further quotations may be in order. First, Kepler wondered whether the mysterious force which moves the planets might be the *light* of the sun. But this could not be; so he went on:

> Though the light of the sun cannot itself be the moving force . . . it may perhaps represent a kind of vehicle, or tool, which the moving force uses. But the following considerations seem to contradict this. Firstly, the light is arrested in regions that lie in shade. If then the moving force were to use light as a vehicle, then darkness would bring the planets to a standstill . . .

This kind of force, just as the kind of force which is light . . . is propagated through the universe . . . but it is nowhere received except where there is a movable body, such as a planet. The answer to this is: although the moving force has no substance, it is aimed at substance, i.e. at the planet-body to be moved . . .

Who, I ask, will pretend that light has substance? Yet nevertheless it acts and is acted upon in space, it is refracted and reflected, and it has quantity, so that it may be dense or sparse, and can be regarded as a plane where it is received by something capable of being lit up. For, as I said in my *Optics*, the same thing applies to light as to our moving force; it has no present existence in the space between the source and the object which it lights up, although it has passed through that space in the past; it 'is' not, it 'was', so to speak.

Thus Kepler's intuitive gropings brought him closer to our contemporary, rather surrealistic concepts of electro-magnetic and gravitational *fields* than to the classic Newtonian concept of force; the modern scientist will find here an echo of his own perplexities. And that may be the reason why Kepler, having hit on the concept of universal gravity, subsequently discarded it—as Galileo was to discard it.

The most precise pre-Newtonian formulations of gravity are to be found in the Preface to the *Astronomia Nova*. Kepler started by refuting the Aristotelian doctrine according to which all 'earthy' matter is heavy because it is its nature to strive towards the centre of the world—that is, the earth, whereas all 'fiery' matter strives by its nature towards the periphery of the universe and is therefore light. Kepler explained that 'heaviness' and 'lightness' are not absolute properties:

Matter that is less dense, either by nature or through heat, is relatively lighter . . . and therefore less attracted [to the earth] than heavier matter . . . Supposing the earth *were* in the centre of the world, heavy bodies would be attracted to it, not because it is in the centre, but because it is a material body. It follows that regardless of where we place the earth, heavenly bodies will always seek it . . .

9

There is a mutual bodily tendency between cognate [i.e. material] bodies towards unity or contact (of which kind the magnetic force also is), so that the earth draws a stone much more than the stone draws the earth . . .

If the earth and the moon were not kept in their respective orbits by a spiritual or some equivalent force, the earth would ascend towards the moon 1/54 of the distance, and the moon would descend the remaining 53 parts of the interval, and thus they would unite. But this calculation presupposes that both bodies are of the same density.

If the earth ceased to attract the waters of the sea, the seas would rise and flow into the moon . . .

If the attractive force of the moon reaches down to the earth, it follows that the attractive force of the earth, all the more, extends to the moon and even farther . . .

If two stones were placed anywhere in space near to each other, and outside the reach of force of a third cognate body, then they would come together, after the manner of magnetic bodies, at an intermediate point, each approaching the other in proportion to the other's mass.

In the same passage is to be found the first approximation to a correct theory of the tides, which Kepler explained as 'a motion of the waters towards the regions where the moon stands in the zenith'. In a work written at the same time—*Somnium—A Dream of the Moon* (an early exercise in science fiction)—he furthermore postulated that the sun's attraction, too, influences the tides—that is, that the gravitational force of the sun reaches as far as the earth.

But here we are faced with another paradox. In the Preface to the *Astronomia Nova*, Kepler, as we have just seen, had grasped the essence of gravity, and even the idea that its force is proportionate to mass; yet in the rest of the book, and in all his subsequent works, *he seems to have completely forgotten it*. The force that emanates from the sun in the Keplerian universe is not a force of attraction but a tangential force, a kind of vortex or 'raging current which tears all the planets, and perhaps all the celestial ether, from West to East'.

To the question of what made Kepler drop gravity no

answer is found anywhere in his profuse writings. Everything points to some unconscious psychological blockage; and we may gather hints about its nature in the writings of the other pioneers of the Scientific Revolution. Thus Galileo indignantly rejected Kepler's suggestion that the tides were due to the moon's attraction, and called it an occult superstition. In the *Dialogue on the Two Great World Systems* he says that Kepler 'despite his open and penetrating mind, lent his ear and his assent to the moon's dominion over the waters, to occult properties [that is, gravity] and such like fancies (*"fanciculezze"*)'.

Descartes was equally repelled by the idea of a non-mechanical force acting at a distance, and, like Kepler, substituted for it vortices in the ether. As for Newton, his attitude is summed up in his famous third letter to Bentley:

> It is inconceivable, that inanimate brute matter should, without the mediation of something else, which is material, operate upon, and affect other matter without mutual contact . . . And this is one reason why I desired you would not ascribe innate gravity to me. That gravity should be innate, inherent, and essential to matter, so that one body may act upon another, at a distance through a vacuum, without the mediation of anything else, by and through which their action and force may be conveyed from one to another, is to me so great an absurdity, that I believe no man who has in philosophical matters a competent faculty of thinking, can ever fall into it . . .

Kepler, Galileo, and Descartes did not fall into the philosophical abyss; their thinking was much too 'modern'— that is, mechanistic—for that. The notion of a 'force' that acts without an intermediary agent and pulls at immense stellar objects with ubiquitous ghost fingers appeared to them mystical and unscientific, a lapse into that Aristotelian animism from which they had just broken loose. Universal gravity, *gravitatio mundi*, smacked of the *anima mundi* of the ancients. Newton overcame the obstacle and made the concept of gravity respectable by invoking the ubiquitous ether, whose attributes, however, were equally paradoxical, so that eventually the whole concept of the ether had to be abandoned. But Newton himself refused to speculate on the manner in which gravity worked,* and even to surmise whether the ether was a 'spiritual' or a 'corporeal' agency. Thus the natural philosophy of the Age of Reason did not rest on quite as solid and reasonable foundations as Pope and his optimistic contemporaries thought . . .

Yet Newton was able to provide a precise mathematical equation for the mysterious agency to which the word gravity referred. That equation was essentially derived from combining the results of Galileo's studies of free fall and the motion of projectiles with Kepler's threee laws of planetary motion. There is no need, in this town of Venice, to enlarge on the genius of Galileo, and the importance of his contribution. But Galileo was a modern, who belongs to the Century of Enlightenment, though he did not live to see it; whereas in Kepler all the contradictions of his age seem to have become incarnate—the age of transition from the mediaeval to the modern world-view. One half of his divided personality belonged to the past; he was a mystic, given to theological speculation, astrology, and number lore. However, he was also an empiricist with a scrupulous respect for observational data, who unhesitatingly threw out his earlier theory of planetary motions, the product of five years of dogged labour, because certain observed positions of Mars deviated from those that the theory demanded by a paltry eight minutes arc. This new-found respect for 'hard obstinate facts' was to determine, to a large extent, the climate of European thought during the next three centuries. It provided Kepler with the necessary discipline and put a restraint on his exuberant fantasy; but the primary motivation of his researches was mysticism of a Pythagorean brand. Throughout his life he was obsessed by certain mystic convictions, each of which had the power of an *idée fixe*. But far from inter-

---

* His famous pronouncement 'hypothesis non fingo' refers to this problem, and to this problem alone, though it is often quoted out of context as a positivistic slogan.

fering with his reasoning powers, these irrational obsessions were harnessed to his rational pursuits and provided the drive for his tireless labours. From a subjective point of view, Kepler's fundamental discoveries were in fact merely by-products of his chimerical quest. I have tried to show how a mystically inspired conviction—which was our starting point—led him to the revolutionary step of projecting physical causation into the skies, to heal the millennial rift between earthly physics and heavenly geometry, and thus to become the founder of modern astronomy. His *Astronomia Nova*, where the First and Second Planetary Laws are found, actually bears the provocative title:

A NEW ASTRONOMY BASED ON CAUSATION OR A PHYSICS OF THE SKY

Another of his obsessions was the belief that the planets' motions were governed by musical harmonies (the Pythagorean 'music of the spheres'); the book containing his Third Law is called *Harmonice Mundi*. Columbus was not the only genius who set out for India and landed in America.

In such crooked ways does the tree of science grow. The curious detours by which Kepler and other pioneers of the Scientific Revolution arrived at their destination may serve as a cautionary tale to scientists and philosophers to remind them of the vast chunks of irrationality embedded in their rational pursuits. The philosophers and encyclopaedists of the *secolo dei lumi* thought that they were living in a solid, rational universe. In fact it was a universe held together by a mysterious force which, like the Holy Ghost, was acting at a distance, in defiance of all the laws of mechanics; and was justifiably rejected by Galileo and other modern-minded thinkers.

This, however, is only one example of the contradictions built into the arrogant rationalism of the Enlightenment. Like the repressed complexes of the Freudians, they were to erupt after a period of latency, with a shattering effect on all established norms, from astronomy to the representative arts.

The Walls of Jericho*

The Babylonian's universe was an oyster with water underneath and more water overhead supported by the vaulted
firmament. It was of moderate dimensions and safely closed
in on all sides like a babe in the womb. From the sixth
pre-Christian century onward, during the heroic age of
Greek science, the oyster was gradually prised open and the
earth set adrift, a huge ball floating unsupported in the air.
The Pythagoreans set the ball spinning; Aristarchus of Samos
set it revolving round the sun; the atomists and Epicureans
dissolved the world's boundaries in the infinite.

This exhilarating development lasted for about three
centuries; when the energies of the heroic age were spent,
the reaction set in. Plato shut the lid of the universe again,
and Aristotle transformed it into an air-tight system of nine
concentric crystal spheres, enclosing each other like the skins
of an onion. The planets moved on smaller spheres, like
ball-bearings between the layers of skin, and the outermost
skin, that of the *primum mobile*, was the boundary of the world.

The Aristotelian model was improved on by Ptolemy, but
the principle remained the same. For nearly two millennia,
the universe went into the deep freeze. Then, in the sixteenth
century, the thaw set in, and was quickly followed by the
scientific and philosophic revolution, which makes the year

* First published in *Encounter*, November 1957.

1600 appear as a kind of watershed in the history of European civilisation. It is at this point that Professor Koyré's book* on the cosmologies of the Renaissance picks up the thread:

> The revolution . . . can be described roughly as bringing forth the destruction of the Cosmos, that is, the disappearance . . . of the conception of the world as a finite, closed, and hierarchically ordered whole (a whole in which the hierarchy of value determined the hierarchy and structure of being rising from the dark, heavy, and imperfect earth to the higher and higher perfection of the stars and heavenly spheres), and its replacement by an indefinite and even infinite universe which is bound together by the identity of its fundamental components and laws, and in which all these components are placed on the same level of being. This, in turn, implies the discarding by scientific thought of all considerations based upon value-concepts, such as perfection, harmony, meaning, and aim, and finally the utter devalorisation of being, the divorce of the world of value and the world of facts.

That lonely, late mediaeval forerunner of the New Philosophy, Bishop Nicholas of Cusa (1401–1464) was the first to kick against the lid of the mediaeval universe; he asserted that the world had no boundaries, and consequently neither periphery nor centre. It was not infinite, merely 'interminate', that is, unbounded. He was no mathematician, and one must beware of reading a too literal interpretation into such intuitive guesses; but in so far as intuition is concerned, Cusa's self-contained universe that is neither closed-in nor infinite, has an unmistakable kinship with the finite, relatavistic universe which, through the curvature of space, returns into itself. But more important: by denying that the world has a centre or a periphery, Cusa denied its hierarchic structure, denied the lowly position which the earth occupied in mediaeval cosmology, the confinement of the evils of 'change and decay' to the sublunary sphere—as opposed to the pure and immutable higher heavens:

* *From the Closed World to the Infinite Universe*, by Alexandre Koyré (The Johns Hopkins Press, Baltimore, 1957; Oxford University Press, London).

The earth is a noble star [Cusa proclaims triumphantly] ... it is not possible for human knowledge to determine whether the region of the earth is in a degree of greater perfection or baseness in relation to the regions of the other stars, of the sun, of the moon, and the rest.

To put it in a pointed manner: a bounded universe, with its concentric series of shells, implies a rigid, hierarchic natural and social order where every (living or inanimate) item in the cosmic inventory has quite literally a 'place' assigned to it in the hierarchy of space; whereas in an infinite or merely unbounded universe, without centre and circumference, no 'place' takes precedence before another— homogeneous space implies a quasi-democratic cosmos. But it also implies, on the debit side, the absence of any obvious, or 'natural', scale of values. Thus the new cosmology was bound to alter the whole pattern of social and moral ideas; and it had, of course, an even more immediate impact on theology and philosophy.

Giordano Bruno, the philosophical *enfant terrible* of the sixteenth century, was the first to assert flatly that the universe was infinite and consisted of an infinite number of inhabited worlds similar to ours: 'Thus is the excellence of God magnified and the greatness of His Kingdom made manifest; he is glorified not in one but in countless suns; not in a single earth, but in a thousand, I say, in an infinity of worlds.' Bruno was an obvious case of being 'drunk with infinity' (as Moses Mendelsohn said of Spinoza); he ended on the stake, though not for his cosmological ideas.

The three giants of the scientific revolution were Galileo, Kepler, and Descartes, whose voices acted on the closed-in mediaeval universe as Joshua's trumpet had on the walls of Jericho. They laid the foundations of the Newtonian universe, but they were characteristically reticent concerning infinity. Kepler rejected it on technical grounds which were quite sound according to the observational data available to him; Galileo shilly-shallied, with an eye on the Inquisition; Descartes, on a higher turn of the spiral, reverted to the position of Cusa: 'We must never dispute about the infinite, but only hold those things to which we do not find any limit, such as the extension of the world . . . to be undefined.'

Descartes' difficulty about the infinite stemmed from the perennial 'horror of the void'; he could neither face an infinite universe filled with matter, nor space without matter. It was again left to a scientific dilettante, the Cambridge Platonist Henry More, to build up a philosophy of infinite space *an sich*—of space as an attribute, not of substance, but of God. Though Newton does not mention More, there is sufficient internal evidence to show that the Newtonian concept of absolute space and time was derived from the latter.

The book ends with an excellent analysis of the famous Newton–Leibnitz controversy about the place and function of God in a mechanised world.

Professor Koyré's previous *magnum opus*, *Études Galiléennes*, was aimed at scholars; his new work is accessible to the educated layman. One of its lessons, as I see it, is, that the dilettantes who made no concrete contribution to science—Bruno, Digges, More, or Coates—developed much sounder and more self-consistent views on the philosophical problems involved in the scientific revolution than the founding fathers of modern physics and astronomy—Copernicus, Galileo, Kepler, Descartes, and Newton himself—who floundered through a mire of contradictions and yet delivered the works. It seems that the saying about good cooks working in dirty kitchens equally applies in the august realms of science.

The Greatest Scandal in Christendom*

'Alas,' the old man of seventy-three wrote to his admirer, Diodati, 'your friend and servant Galileo has been for the last month hopelessly blind; so that this heaven, this earth, this universe, which I, by marvellous discoveries and clear demonstrations, have enlarged a hundred thousand times beyond the belief of the wise men of bygone ages, henceforward for me is shrunk into such small space as is filled by my own bodily sensations. . . .'

All the main ingredients are there, contained in a few lines: the grandeur, the boastfulness, the self-pity, the elegance of style.

The letter is dated from Galileo's villa, *Il Giojello*, at Arcetri where he spent the last years of his life. It stands on a hill among olive groves overlooking Florence, but its name, the jewel, sounds today sadly ironical. The garden, where he received Milton and a stream of other celebrities, is covered with weeds; the sixteenth-century house, with its old beams and high ceilings, is occupied by tenants and contains no trace of the past. On the outside of the massive stone wall which separates the garden from the one and only street of the

*First published in *The Observer* on the 400th anniversary of Galileo's birth, February 1964.

village of Arcetri, there is a sort of niche containing an old marble *pissoir* without a door or screen; close to it is a decayed memorial plaque with a bust of Galileo sternly watching the urinators. Whether this is intended as a deliberate insult—a kind of *Clochemerle* in reverse—I was unable to discover; but it certainly testifies to a lack of reverence of the powers that be towards the memory of the man who, in the words of his one-time admirer, Pope Urban VIII, had 'given rise to the greatest scandal throughout Christendom'. Its shadow still lingers over the desolate house.

The scandal is one of the historic causes which made post-Renaissance Europe a divided house of faith and reason. Legend has turned Galileo into a martyr of the freedom of thought, Urban into its benighted oppressor, and the conflict into a kind of Greek tragedy ennobled by the stamp of historical inevitability. In fact it was a clash of temperaments wantonly provoked and aggravated by unlucky coincidences.

To understand what really happened, a word must be said about the background—the grand topography of the universe, as Galileo's contemporaries saw it.

For the last two thousand years, according to the orthodox doctrine, the solid earth had been regarded as the centre of the world round which the sun, the planets and the stars revolved in their orbits; it was based on the legacy of Aristotle and had been elaborated in detail by Ptolemy, an Alexandrian astronomer of the second century A.D. As against this there existed another grand scheme of even more ancient origin. The Pythagorean school, which had flourished between the fifth and third centuries B.C., had taught that the earth rotated on its own axis; and at least one Pythagorean, Aristarchus of Samos, held that in addition to its daily rotation, the earth also travelled through space in its annual revolutions round the sun; the five known planets did the same, so that the sun, and not the earth, was the centre and hub of the universe.

The geocentric system of Aristotle and Ptolemy had prevailed, but the rival heliocentric system of the Pythagoreans was never quite forgotten. It was preserved in the writings of the Latin compilers; it was finally revived and elaborated in detail by Canon Koppernigk or Copernick, called Copernicus, a somewhat crotchety cleric in the God-forsaken province of Varmia on the Baltic Sea.

Copernicus had died in 1543, twenty-one years before Galileo was born; his book, *On the Revolutions of the Heavenly Spheres*, which outlined the heliocentric system, was published in the last year of his life. For more than half a century it aroused very little interest. It was addressed, as the title page said, 'to mathematicians only', it was clumsily written, and marred by inconsistencies. The reaction of the academic world was, with a few exceptions, indifferent or hostile, as Copernicus had feared; it was this fear 'to be laughed at and hissed off the stage' (to quote his own words) which had caused him to withhold publication of the *Book of the Revolutions* until the end of his life.

What made him finally overcome his apprehensions were the urgent entreaties of his superiors in the ecclesiastical hierarchy who had read manuscript outlines of his theory. In 1533, Pope Clement VII had listened to a lecture on the Copernican theory, and was favourably impressed; a few years later, Cardinal Schönberg, who occupied positions of special trust under three successive Popes, wrote to the humble canon in Varmia that he had learned with great admiration about Copernicus' 'having created a new theory of the Universe according to which the Earth moves and the sun occupies the basic and central position. . . . Therefore, learned man, without wishing to be inopportune, I beg you most emphatically to communicate your discovery to the learned world. . . .'

Copernicus printed the letter as a preface to his book, which he dedicated to Clement's successor, Paul III. Thus, contrary to legend, the Church did not initially oppose the theory of the motion of the earth. The opposite is true. Without the encouragement and patronage of the clergy—from the Bishop of Varmia to circles close to the Vatican—Canon

Copernicus' book would never have seen the light of day. Nor did the attitude of the Church change for the next eighty years.

Galileo became converted to the Copernican system in his twenties. But he kept his convictions secret until he was nearly fifty, although he had no more reason to fear religious persecution than Copernicus had. Through all these years he taught in his lectures the old astronomy of Ptolemy, and expressly repudiated the earth's motion by means of the traditional arguments (the clouds would be left behind, etc.) which he knew to be false. This fact is passed over in silence by Galileo's biographers, although it is an important clue to his character.*

The reason why he kept his opinions so carefully concealed was the same as in Copernicus' case: the fear of ridicule by his narrow-minded colleagues who occupied the chairs of astronomy in Bologna, Pisa, Padua and elsewhere. In a letter to the German astronomer, Johannes Kepler (the first to raise his voice in public for Copernicus, fifteen years before Galileo), he confessed: 'I have not dared to bring my views into the public light, frightened by the fate of Copernicus himself, our teacher, who, though he acquired immortal fame with some, was yet by an infinite multitude of others— for such is the number of fools—laughed at and hissed off the stage.' The risk of ecclesiastic censure did not even occur to him because, during the first fifty years of his lifetime, no such risk existed. Even his latest apologist, Giorgio de Santillana, admitted: 'On his [Galileo's] own account, he knew the Jesuits as modern-minded humanists, friends of science and discovery. Those he feared were the professors.'† And that fear, as events proved, was fully justified.

*   *   *

* The proof is found in a surviving manuscript copy of a lecture by Galileo, dated 1606, *Trattato della Sfera* (*Opere, Ediz. Nazionale*, Florence; 1929–30, Vol. II, pp. 203–55).

† *The Crime of Galileo* (Cambridge, 1955), p. 8.

In 1610, when he was forty-six, Galileo's life took a dramatic turn. He was then Professor of Mathematics in Padua, much admired by his friends for his revolutionary researches in physics—which he communicated to them in private letters —but as yet untouched by public fame. Fame came almost overnight through his astronomical discoveries, made possible by that newly invented gadget, the telescope. It was invented by a Dutchman, but Galileo built his own instruments with a vastly improved magnifying power. He published his observations in a booklet' *Siderius Nuncius*—the 'Star Messenger'. It described the mountainous configurations of the moon, the dissolution of the Milky Way into 'a map of unnumerable stars planted together in clusters', and left the most momentous news to the last—that the planet Jupiter possessed four moons 'never seen from the beginning of the world up to our times'. This did not prove that the Copernican scheme of the universe was right, but it shattered the orthodox doctrine that the earth was the centre of the world around which everything revolved—the Jupiter moons danced attendance to a rival body.

The 'Star Messenger' created a sensation. Cardinal del Monte, one of Galileo's patrons, wrote in a letter: 'If we were still living under the ancient Republic of Rome, I verily believe that there would be a column on the Capitol erected in Galileo's honour.' The Jesuits of the Roman College, who were the leading astronomers of the day, bestowed ceremonial honours on him; Pope Paul V received him in a long audience. Yet barely five years later an edict of the Holy Office condemned the Copernican theory as incompatible with Holy Scripture, and Galileo was enjoined, by order of Pope Paul, not to 'hold or defend' it.

On whom does the historic responsibility rest? In the first place on 'the professors', the academic mediocrity, who hated Galileo, partly out of jealousy, partly because they were the rearguard of those Schoolmen whom Erasmus had accused of 'looking in utter darkness for that which has no existence whatsoever'. They were so dazzled by what the telescope revealed that several of them, like the illustrious Cremonini, refused on principle to look through it; and those who did look pretended that the Jupiter-moons were optical illusions. But eventually the 'Pigeon League'—as Galileo contemptuously called them after their leader, Lodovico delle Colombe—had to accept defeat, when the élite of the Jesuit astronomers at their observatories in various parts of Europe not only confirmed Galileo's discoveries, but improved on them.

At this point Galileo's vanity played him a trick which had disastrous results. For more than twenty years he had believed in the Copernican system but had taught the opposite. Now, encouraged by his success, he had come out into the open; and once he had committed himself to the Copernican theory anybody who opposed it was to be regarded as a 'mental pygmy', 'hardly deserving to be called a human being'.

But he had no scientific proof that the Copernican system was correct. The point is somewhat technical, but basic to the understanding of the whole drama. The Jupiter moons and other phenomena proved that Aristotle had been wrong —they did not prove that Copernicus had been right. There existed alternative possibilities—such as the compromise system of Tycho de Brahe, in which the planets revolved round the sun, and the sun round the earth. It was a half-way house, but from the point of view of mathematical calculation just as satisfactory as the Copernican system—and the available data spoke in favour of Tycho and against Copernicus. For if the earth really moved round the sun, then its position relative to the fixed stars must differ by nearly two hundred million miles every six months, and their constellations ought to expand and shrink according to whether the earth approached or receded from them. But in spite of the thousandfold magnification of Galileo's telescopes, no such effect was found (it was only found two centuries later by Bessel). Thus not only tradition, prejudice and naïve 'commonsense', but also the scientific evidence available at the time, spoke *against* the Copernican theory.

Galileo was well aware of this. So were his enemies. But since they had been defeated in the controversy on the Jupiter moons and in several other disputes, they knew they were no match either for his genius or his polemical brilliance. So the Pigeon League shifted its ground from science to theology. They produced quotations from Holy Scripture in refutation of Copernicus. Thus Joshua, after defeating the Philistines, had cried 'Sun, stand thou still'—which proved clearly that it was the sun which moved, not the earth.

Galileo fell into the trap. In two treatises, which he circulated widely in manuscript copies ('Letter to Castelli', 1613, enlarged a year later into "Letter to the Grand Duchess Christina'), he dived headlong into theology. He evaded any scientific discussion of the Copernican system by simply pretending that it was proven beyond doubt; proposed that biblical passages which contradicted it should be re-interpreted, and insisted that the Church must either endorse the Copernican theory or condemn it altogether. This made a showdown unavoidable.

Galileo's friends in the upper ranks of the Church hierarchy—foremost among them Maffeo Barberini, the future Pope—did everything in their power to avoid the showdown. When the monks of St. Marco in Florence denounced the 'Letter to Castelli', the Holy Office dismissed the case. When a Dominican by the name of Caccini attacked Galileo from the pulpit, the Preacher General of the Order promptly wrote him a letter of apology. The official attitude of the Church was summed up by its highest theological authority: Cardinal Bellarmine, General of the Jesuit Order, Consultor to the Holy Office (the 'devilish Jebusite' whom the English suspected of having instigated the Gunpowder Plot). In a letter to Father Foscarini, a Carmelite monk who had just published a book advocating the Copernican system, but equally addressed to Galileo, who is mentioned by name, Bellarmine explained that to teach the Copernican system *as a working hypothesis* superior to Ptolemy's 'is to speak with excellent sense and to run no risk whatever. Such a manner of speaking suffices for a mathematician.' But to speak of it *as an established truth* 'is a very dangerous attitude and one calculated not only to arouse the Scholastic philosophers and theologians, but also to injure our holy faith by contradicting the Scriptures'. However, Bellarmine continued, *if* there existed a 'real proof' which 'truly demonstrated' the earth's motion, *then* the relevant passages in the Scriptures would have to be re-interpreted. 'But I do not think there is any such proof since none has been shown to me.'

Bellarmine's ruling reflected not only the established practice of the Church in such matters; its substance would also have been endorsed by any responsible body of modern empirical scientists. But Galileo was past reasoning. To admit that the Copernican system was no more than an unproven hypothesis, however excellent, would amount to the confession that he had no evidence to offer, and expose him to the ridicule of his opponents. There is hardly a more frustrating experience for a scientist than to *know* that one is right, but to be unable to prove it—and to be 'hissed off the stage' by an audience of imbeciles. Against the warnings of Bellarmine and other friendly cardinals, Galileo rushed to Rome, to force a decision. 'He is passionately involved in this quarrel' the Tuscan Ambassador reported, 'so that he will be snarled in it and get himself into danger. . . . For he is vehement and all impassioned in this affair.'

He tried unsuccessfully for an audience with Paul V, who (as the same Ambassador described him) 'abhors the liberal arts and cannot stand these novelties and subtleties'. Which particular incident brought matters to a head is still a matter of controversy, and without much importance. Galileo had insisted on a showdown; he had gambled and lost.

On March 5, 1616, the Holy Office issued a decree in which 'the Pythagorean doctrine of the motion of the earth' was declared to be 'false and altogether opposed to Holy Scripture'; to prevent its further spreading, Copernicus's

25

Book of the Revolutions was 'suspended until it be corrected'. It actually remained on the Index for no more than four years; the corrections consisted in the change or omission of altogether nine sentences in which the heliocentric system was represented as a certainty instead of a hypothesis. Galileo's name was not mentioned in the decree, his works were not prohibited, and to save him from public humiliation the injunction not to hold or defend the Copernican doctrine was communicated to him privately. To sweeten the pill even more, a week after publication of the decree, the Pope received Galileo in a long audience.

Thus the first act of the scandal ended on a decorous note; yet it injected a poison into the atmosphere of our culture which is still there. Act II came seventeen years later.

The main event of the intervening years was the election to the Papacy of Galileo's most ardent admirer, Cardinal Maffeo Barberini. He had opposed the decree of 1616; he had written an ode in honour of Galileo; when he became Pope, he gave Galileo a testimonial extolling the virtues and piety 'of this great man, whose fame shines in the heavens and goes on earth far and wide'. In 1624, a year after he had been installed as Urban VIII, he gave Galileo six long audiences in six weeks, showering gifts and favours on him.

Maffeo Barberini was a brilliant, vainglorious cynic who did not care much whether Copernicus contradicted the miracle of Joshua or not. On learning of Richelieu's death, he coined the famous epigram: 'If God exists, Cardinal Richelieu will have much to answer for; if not, he has done very well.' His vanity was as monumental as Galileo's; he professed 'to know better than all cardinals put together' as Galileo professed to be the 'sole discoverer of all celestial novelties'. It needed no great psychiatric insight to predict the end of the affair.

Though Urban could not revoke the edict of 1616, he paid homage to the memory of Copernicus; and after those six long audiences, Galileo returned from Rome to Florence, reassured that he could now expound the Copernican system on condition that he stuck to the established rules of the game: to avoid theological arguments, and to speak of the earth's motion as a convenient *working hypothesis* without asserting that it was *actually true*.

This sounds reasonable enough. But Galileo's temperament made it impossible for him to abide by the rules—and on this point every writer with strong convictions must sympathise with him. Besides, he thought that at long last he had found a physical proof for the motion of the earth (we remember that it was the lack of proof which had made him lose the first round of the battle). The proof was contained in his famous theory of the tides. Rejecting Kepler's correct suggestion that the tides were caused by the moon's attraction, Galileo had persuaded himself that the seas 'swapped over' once a day as a direct consequence of the earth's motion. Here, then, was the evidence he had been so desperately looking for. It was a fallacy in such glaring contradiction to all the principles of the science of dynamics which he himself had discovered, and so unworthy of his genius, that it can be explained only as an *idée fixe*.

The years that followed were spent in writing his great apologia for the Copernican theory, the *Dialogue on the Two Great World Systems*. It is perhaps the most brilliant and exasperating work among the books which made history. Masterly expositions alternate in it with special pleading, immortal passages with cheap rhetoric and the deliberate falsification of facts. The theory of the tides occupies a central position, and serves to clinch the argument. Whatever the contemporary reader's reaction to the book, one point was made abundantly clear to him: that the earth's motion was *not* merely a working hypothesis but a fact so firmly established that it could be doubted only by 'dumb mooncalves' whose stupidity 'stains the honour of mankind'.

Thus the contents of the book were a flagrant contravention of the decree of 1616, and of the line agreed on with

Urban VIII. But there were still other circumstances which precipitated the scandal. Galileo had obtained the *imprimatur* for the book by a series of manoeuvres which amounted to a confidence trick. He had antagonised his former supporters, the Jesuit astronomers, by laying unfounded priority claims to their discoveries, and engaging them in controversies on irrelevant subjects; it was as if he were acting under some self-destructive compulsion. Lastly, he had personally insulted the Pope. In the days of their mutual adulation, Urban had suggested an argument which would enable Galileo to speak favourably of the Copernican theory without asserting its actual truth. The argument was, briefly, that even if a hypothesis explains certain phenomena in a satisfactory manner, it need not necessarily be true, for God may have produced the same phenomena by different means, not comprehended by the human mind. This argument, to which Urban attached the greatest importance, is quoted only at the very end of the book; and the character who quotes it is Simplicio, the simpleton of the *Dialogue*, who has been shown up as a silly ass over and over again. Galileo might as well have stuck out his tongue in public at the Pope.

Contrary to legend, Nemesis took a rather leisurely course. The book was published in February 1632. It was not until August that its sale was suspended, and a commission appointed to examine its contents. The commissioners indicted it on eight counts, but concluded that 'all these matters could be corrected if it is decided that the book is of any value'. The report was then handed over to the Inquisition, which, in October, summoned Galileo to Rome. Galileo sent a medical certificate from Florence, attesting that he was suffering from 'attacks of giddiness, hypochondriacal melancholy, weakness of stomach, insomnia, and flying pains about the body'; he thus succeeded in delaying his journey till February 1633. In Rome, he took up quarters in the Villa Medici, which was then the Tuscan

Embassy, and another three months passed before he was summoned for his first interrogation by the Commissary of the Inquisition, Firenzuola.

From April 12 to May 10, while the proceedings lasted, he was formally a prisoner of the Inquisition; in fact he occupied a five-room flat in the Holy Office overlooking the Vatican Gardens, shared by his valet, while the Tuscan Ambassador's majordomo looked after his food and wine. He never spent a day of his life in a prison cell, and was neither tortured nor in fear of torture—which, according to the rules of the Roman Inquisition, could not be inflicted on a man of his age. (The Spanish Inquisition was, of course, an altogether different matter.)

In short, the authorities treated Galileo with all the lenience and regard due to the foremost scholar of his time; d with that disregard for the freedom of thought which was engrained in their tradition and doctrine. They did not intend to turn him into a martyr, but rather to show that he was not of the stuff of which martyrs are made; to humiliate him, make him recant, and prove that not even a Galileo could allow himself to mock the Pope and challenge the authority of the theologians.

The legal proceedings were highly unorthodox. In the very first interrogation Galileo manoeuvred himself into an impossible position by pretending, in the teeth of the printed evidence, that his book was written with the intention not to support but to *refute* the Copernican theory. The only possible explanation of this folly is a failure of nerve. He had thought himself capable of outwitting Urban and everybody else; on being found out he realised that the game was up and he panicked.

Nothing happened for a fortnight. Then Firenzuola went on a private, 'extrajudicial' visit to Galileo's apartment, and had no great difficulty in persuading him to make a deal. Soon afterwards he was allowed to return to the Villa Medici; another month later, on June 22, Galileo was conducted to a hall in the Convent of Santa Maria sopra

Minerva, where in the presence of his judges—ten Cardinals, only seven of whom had concurred—the sentence was read out to him. The *Dialogue* was to be prohibited; to clear himself from the suspicion of heresy he was to recite a prepared text cursing and abjuring the doctrine of the earth's motion; and he was to be committed to 'formal prison during the Holy Office's pleasure'. Then the vain old man went down on his knees before the venal Cardinals, recited a text in which nobody believed, wisely refrained from saying *eppur si muove*, and the show-trial was over.

'Formal prison' meant, first, a sojourn with the Grand Duke of Tuscany, then with the Archbishop of Siena, followed by ten peaceful and creative years in the villa at Arcetri, where he wrote his masterpiece, the *Dialogue Concerning Two New Sciences*. It became one of the cornerstones of the Scientific Revolution, and made Galileo rank among the intellectual giants who shaped the destiny of the world.

His true greatness rests on achievements which have nothing to do with the Galileo legend. He never dropped cannonballs from the leaning tower of Pisa, made no contribution to theoretical astronomy, and did not prove the earth's motion. His real achievements are those found in every schoolbook: the laws of the pendulum, of free fall, of the flight of projectiles, of the elasticity, cohesion and resistance of solid bodies, and a hundred related matters. He was a pioneer of the experimental method and transformed physics into an exact, mathematical science. This was his vocation; not the ill-starred propaganda crusade based on fallacious arguments, which cost him twenty years of his life and ended in disaster.

It nearly put an end to three centuries of that peaceful coexistence between faith and reason which had started with Thomas of Aquinas, and saw Franciscans, Dominicans, Jesuits successively take the lead in the revival of learning, and the advance of science. Throughout the golden age of humanism and well into the seventeenth century, scientists like Copernicus and Galileo were the protégés of cardinals and popes; and the exploration of the laws of nature was regarded as a form of worship of the Supreme Mathematician.

The Galileo scandal marked a turning point—a hardening of the fronts, the polarisation of rigid orthodoxies. The point I have been trying to make is that the blame was not all on one side; that the presumption of the theologians was matched by the *hubris* of an unbalanced genius and the vindictiveness of a benighted academic coterie. And concerning the latter, though methods have changed, it can hardly be said that behind the polite façades academic orthodoxy has become much more tolerant. The Inquisition at least has gone, and the Bishop of Woolwich has not been excommunicated; but the Pigeon Leagues are still flourishing in the Groves of Academe.

Artist on a Tightrope

*Inaugural Address at the Symposium on 'Belief and Literature',
Calcutta, February 1959**

In 1942, I made friends with a young fighter pilot, Richard
Hillary. He had been shot down in flames in the Battle of
Britain when he was not quite twenty. His earlier photographs showed him as an extremely attractive young man;
when I met him, his burnt and shrivelled hands were like
birds' claws and his face a mask of plastic surgery. He was
given a job by the Ministry of Information, published a book
The Last Enemy, which instantly became a bestseller, had an
attractive mistress, and led a pleasant life in London. Yet
after a couple of years of this, he tricked the Medical Board
into certifying him fit for active service, returned to flying,
and was killed a few months later in an accident while
training to become a night fighter.

His letters from this last period described a kind of double
existence he was leading at the aerodrome. During the day,
his burnt body suffered from the intense cold; he was bored,
frightened, irritated. But at night—as he described in a
letter—'I have only to step into an aeroplane—that

* Some of the illustrations in this lecture I used again in *The Sleepwalkers* and *The Act of Creation.*

monstrous thing of iron and steel just watching for its chance to down me—and all fear goes. I am at peace again . . .'

We discussed this dualism of experience; my letters to him were lost, but he summed up what I was trying to say better than I could have done. In a letter to a third person, he wrote:*

> K. has a theory for this. He believes there are two planes of existence which he calls *vie tragique* and *vie triviale*. Usually we move on the trivial plane, but occasionally in moments of elation or danger, we find ourselves transferred to the plane of the *vie tragique*, with its non-commonsense, cosmic perspective. When we are on the trivial plane, the realities of the other appear as nonsense—as overstrung nerves, and so on. When we live on the tragic plane, the joys and sorrows of the other are shallow, frivolous, trifling. But in exceptional circumstances, for instance, if one has to live through a long stretch of time in physical danger, one is placed, as it were, on the intersection line of the two planes; a curious situation which is a kind of tightrope-walking on one's nerves . . . I think he is right.

So far Hillary, the pilot. But there is another type of person condemned to walk on the intersection line of the two planes: the artist. For this meeting of the trivial narrative of life with its tragic essence (a meeting which in the average citizen's curriculum only occurs in a few solemnly catastrophic moments of danger, death or unhappy love) is the very essence of art. Art is the gift—or curse—of perceiving the trivial objects and events of everyday experience *sub specie eternitatis*; and conversely, to express the absolute in human terms, to reflect it in a concrete image. 'The infinite is made to blend itself with the finite; to stand visible, as it were, attainable here. Of this sort are all true works of art; in this we discern eternity looking through time' (Carlyle).

Now there are various ways in which literature can become such a window in time, in which the intersection of the two planes is achieved. The tragic plane of experience

* Cf. 'In Memory of Richard Hillary' in *The Yogi and the Commissar* (1945).

33

may be more or less conscious, more or less articulated. It may, for instance, be projected into the symbols expressed in the archetypal images of myth, folklore and religion. It may be felt and not stated: the actual words may be not more than the vibrations of a tuning fork, which makes the reader resonate without knowing why. Lichtenberg said that the works of the Protestant mystic Jacob Boehme were 'like a picnic where the host provides the words and the guests provide the meaning'.

On the opposite end of the scale, we have the articulate type of narrative literature in which the cosmic plane manifests itself in the shape of an ideology. I am using here the word 'ideology' in the broad sense of a system of co-ordinates, a grid of perception, a hierarchy of values derived from certain beliefs about the ultimate nature of reality and the meaning of existence. Again, this ideology may be stated explicitly or merely implied. Allow me to quote an early example of ideological literature: the Biblical story of Jonah and the Whale.

Jonah is described in the story as a decent fellow who has committed no crime to warrant his dreadful punishment. This very ordinary person receives a sudden order from God 'to go to Nineveh, that great city, and cry against it'—which is a rather tall order; he understandably prefers to go on leading his happy and trivial life. So, evading the call from the Tragic Plane, he buys a passage on a ship to Tarshish; and he has such a clean conscience about it that while the storm rages Jonah is peacefully asleep. And therein precisely lies his sin—in his normality, in his complacency, in his refusal to face the storm and the corruption of Nineveh— therein lies his sin, according to the narrator's idea, which must be punished in the belly of the whale:

> The waters compassed me about . . . the weeds were wrapped about my head . . . *yet hast thou brought up my life from corruption, O Lord my God . . . They that observe lying vanities forsake their own mercy.*

In none of the ancient civilisations was the tension between the Tragic and Trivial Planes more intensely felt than by the Hebrews. Jonah's only crime was trying to lead a normal life and to disregard the terrible voice from that other plane of existence. Melville understood this when, in the great sermon in *Moby Dick*, he made his preacher sum up the lesson of Jonah:

> Woe to him who seeks to pour oil upon the waters when God has brewed them into a gale! Woe to him who seeks to please rather than to appal! . . . Woe to him who, in this world, courts not dishonour!

Contrast this with Candide's 'Let us cultivate our little garden', or the Buddha's 'Middle Way'. The astonishing thing is that both ideologies seem equally plausible, convincing, self-evident—because they are expressed not in propaganda pamphlets, but works of art. But let us have no illusions about the 'objectivity' of art. There is always an ideology behind it, however indirectly stated, because all art attempts to answer a tragic question and each answer implies a programme—or at least an attitude to life.

Let me take a second example from a period more than two millennia later. I shall read you an oft-quoted passage from the great peroration of Ulysses in the first act of *Troilus and Cressida*. I hope you will agree that the passage is poetically strong and expressive, but I fear that you will also find it rather confusing and meaningless if you are not familiar with the ideological framework behind it:

> The heavens themselves, the planets, and this centre
> Observe degree, priority, and place,
> Insisture, course, proportion, season, form,
> Office, and custom, in all line of order:
> . . . but when the planets,
> In evil mixture, to disorder wander,
> What plagues and what portents! what mutiny!
> What raging of the sea! shaking of earth!
> Commotion in the winds! frights, changes, horrors,
> Divert and crack, rend and deracinate

> The unity and married calm of states
> Quite from their fixture! O, when degree is shak'd,
> Which is the ladder to all high designs,
> The enterprise is sick! . . .
> Take but degree away, untune that string,
> And, hark, what discord follows! each thing meets
> In mere oppugnancy: the bounded waters
> Should lift their bosoms higher than the shores
> And make a sop of all this solid globe:
> Strength should be lord of imbecility,
> And the rude son should strike his father dead.

Well, you may ask, what is all this excitement about? What is the cause of this apocalyptic vision, what is the valiant Ulysses so afraid of?

The key word of the passage is the word 'degree': 'The heavens themselves, the planets and this centre (the earth) observe degree, priority and place.' And later on: 'O, when degree is shak'd, the enterprise is sick.' To us the word 'degree' is rather abstract and unpoetical, but to the Elizabethan audience in the theatre it was a familiar allusion to a view of the world, a philosophy that was taken for granted. It was a view based on Christian doctrine, Neoplatonic philosophy and Aristotelian cosmology—the universe as Dante, Shakespeare and the Elizabethan poets saw it.

It was a walled-in universe like a walled-in mediaeval town; in its centre was the earth—dark, heavy and corrupt, surrounded by the nine concentric crystal spheres of the moon, sun, planets and stars, each representing a higher degree of perfection, up to the abode of God. To this hierarchic order of *space* was attached a hierarchy of *rank* and *value* which stretched down like a ladder from the supreme ruler of the universe, through the hierarchy of angels, which kept the crystal spheres of the stars spinning, down to man. Here on earth, the *cosmic* ladder continued as a *social* ladder with its hierarchy of kings, barons, knights, commoners, and serfs, then down through the animal, vegetable and mineral kingdom into inanimate nature; and further down into a conic cavity in the earth, around whose narrowing slopes the nine hierarchies of devils are arranged in circles duplicating the nine heavenly spheres.

In this rigid, static, petrified universe, every *change* that would confuse the order of the cosmic ladder was regarded as a universal catastrophe because, owing to the rigidity of the system, the disturbance would immediately spread both up and down the ladder: 'O, when degree is shak'd, the enterprise is sick . . . What raging of the sea! . . . frights, *changes*, horrors.' Notice that the word 'change' stands between 'frights' and 'horrors' and was regarded as a synonym in that fear-ridden age.

I would further like to call your attention to the passage, 'Take but degree away, *untune that string*, and hark what discord follows'. The musical imagery here is not just a poetical metaphor, but a concrete allusion to another ideological concept: the harmony of the spheres. This concept originated with Pythagoras in the sixth century B.C. and was again much in fashion following the Platonic revival of the Renaissance. The harmony of the spheres was supposed to be a celestial music produced by the planets as they swish through space, each at a different speed. According to legend, Pythagoras was the only man who was actually able to *hear* the music of the spheres, because ordinary mortals were too grossly constituted. That both Shakespeare and his audience were familiar with this concept can be gathered from a number of similar passages. Thus, for instance, in *The Merchant of Venice*, Lorenzo explains it to Jessica:

> . . . soft stillness and the night
> Become the touches of sweet harmony . . .
> There's not the smallest orb which thou behold'st
> But in his motion like an angel sings . . .
> Such harmony is in immortal souls:
> But, whilst this muddy vesture of decay
> Doth grossly close it in, we cannot hear it.

If you are interested in this particular subject, I would refer you to Professor Tillyard's *The Elizabethan World*

Picture. The purpose of my quoting these examples was to demonstrate that even the most timeless works of literature, without any apparent ideological bias, will reveal under the X-ray camera a scaffolding of moral values and philosophical assumptions. There is no game without rules of the game, and there is no work of art without some working hypothesis behind it.

In this sense, but only in this sense, all literature is committed, is a *litterature engagée*. This leads to two opposite dangers: firstly the literature *engagée* may degenerate into a literature *enragée*, as happened with the Marxist literature of 'thirties, and again recently in the French existentialist circus. Conversely, the yearning to escape one's ideological chains may end in escapism, the evading of all worthwhile problems.

Concerning the first of these dangers, we know that the artist's mission is not to preach, but demonstrate. We are aware of the difference between art and propaganda, between the universal and the topical—but it is not always easy to draw a line between the two; and even a Tolstoy did not always succeed in drawing it.

The second danger, the flight into the ivory tower, is much in evidence in the contemporary English novel. Our Book Society choices are still teeming with young ladies in old country houses who amble through mellow gardens with a tennis racket in one hand and a volume of Proust in the other. Mind you, I do not miss the hydrogen bomb in the dialogue, but I miss it in the author's consciousness. To create innocence, one must have awareness of guilt. To define the position of a point in space, one must have a system of co-ordinates. And every system of co-ordinates has the curious attribute that it embraces the whole infinity of space.

And thus at the end I am back at my starting point. All true art is a tightrope walk on the line of intersection of the tragic and trivial planes of existence. When the acrobat slips, art degenerates into propaganda, or escapes into a bloodless cloud-cuckoo land; it ceases to be art. Walking the tightrope is a tricky profession.

The Age of Discretion

Broadcast on the B.B.C. Third Programme, February 25, 1960.

Nineteen-sixty means to me *anno* 15 p.H., where 'p' stands for *post*, and 'H' stands for Hiroshima. I say that not because I like to remember that episode, nor as an act of penance—for after all we were not consulted—but for a factual and unsentimental reason. Calendars imply convictions about the importance of certain events: the first Olympiad for the Greeks, the foundation of the city of Rome, the birth of a child in Bethlehem, the flight of Mohammed from Mecca. The positing of a year zero provides a time-scale, a measure of the age, of the distance covered, from the real or assumed starting point, of a given civilisation.

There is, I believe, a strong case to be made for keeping a kind of second calendar in our minds which indicates the distance travelled from that decisive moment when a man-made flash of light outshone the sun. Fifteen years are but a few seconds on the dials of history, and it is not surprising that this new-born civilisation of ours is as yet unaware of its own separate existence. More precisely, its awareness is still of that inchoate, shapeless, nebulous kind which precedes the young child's discovery of its identity. On the surface we find no sharp, decisive break between life before and after *anno* zero. There have been some social, political, cultural changes, but if these were all there would be no justification for suggesting this kind of new calendar.

My feeling that all that happened before 1945 belongs to a quasi-prehistorical epoch is based on a rather simple consideration which, however, is not quite simple to explain. Let me proceed by steps. The fact that mankind has acquired the power to destroy itself does enter into it, but merely as a preliminary step. The next question is what this fact does to the human psyche. I think that, so far, it has affected it very little, at least on the conscious level. The simple proof is that everybody went on manufacturing the thing. There were, there are, protests and involved controversies, but no global outcry powerful enough to stop it. The somewhat clownish character of some of the protest demonstrations is particularly revealing. The voluble phrases about the possibility of blowing the whole planet to glory sounded at first both frightening and subtly flattering to our vanity; but soon they became clichés divorced from emotional meaning. Then everybody got bored with this insoluble problem until the sputniks and satellites brought a new thrill, and the pleasant hope that these things might develop a tendency to keep going upward and not coming down.

And thus, *anno* 15 p.H., we have apparently settled down to business as usual. But, I believe, only apparently. There are periods of incubation. The Copernican theory of the earth's motion took eighty years before it began to sink in. The unconscious has its own clock, and its own ways of digesting what the conscious mind has rejected as indigestible. There are signs that, on a limited scale and in an oblique way, this process of assimilation has already begun—a process which, I believe, is bound to transform completely the mental make-up of our race. The essence of this transformation could be defined as follows: hitherto man had to live with the idea of his death as an individual; from now onward mankind will have to live with the idea of its death as a species.

This is an entirely novel prospect, but not necessarily a

gloomy one. To realise its implications one must try to bear in mind that we are not dealing in abstractions but with hard, obstinate facts; in other words, we must try to achieve a psychological break-through across the multiple smoke-screen of our own mental defences against reality. If we succeed in achieving that, we may discover a rather breath-taking vision beyond the screen, which will make human destiny appear in a new light. We who were brought up in the Western way of thinking have always been taught to accept the transitoriness of our existence as individuals, while taking the survival of our species axiomatically for granted. And this was a perfectly reasonable belief, barring some unlikely cosmic catastrophe. But it has ceased to be a reasonable belief since the day, fifteen years ago, when the feasibility of just such a cosmic catastrophe was tested and proven. It pulverised the assumptions on which all philo-sophy, from Socrates onward, was based; that is to say, the potential immortality of our species.

Let us consider the implications of this turn of events from a completely detached, that is, from an inhuman, point of view. Let us imagine that among the hidden works of the Lord Almighty there functions a kind of inter-galactic insurance company which periodically surveys the insurance risks which the various intelligent species on the various inhabited planets represent. The insurance company knows no more about the intellectual progress and psychological kinks of its individual clients—which number perhaps half a million species in our galaxy alone—than a terrestrial insur-ance company does. It simply watches them from a distance. Before its observers noticed that certain flash fifteen years ago, they would probably have given the inhabitants of this planet quite a reasonable life-span. It has, by cosmic stan-dards, just the right size of a middle-aged sun, in a stable, middle-aged galaxy, safe by all probability standards from any local or inter-galactic collision. Its dominant race, which emerged relatively late after the beginning of organic life on the planet, seemed to be intellectually precocious, emotionally retarded, and accordingly maladjusted. But against this it enjoyed the considerable advantage of having no serious biological competitors for the mastery of the planet. So far, so good. Then came the familiar flash which the company's watchmen had so frequently observed in other parts of the sky, and the computers were set to work.

The computers worked on the principle, based on past experience, that the gadgets which cause the flash will undergo the process known as progressive miniaturisation: they will become ever smaller and more elegant, as suitcases and transistor radios and satellite equipment did. The computers accordingly took it for granted that an effective global control of the gadgets was in the long run impracticable on these grounds alone, and that in the foreseeable future they will be produced and stored in large quantities, from windswept Alaska to sunny Cairo and Tel Aviv. The computers were then fed relevant samples of the past behaviour of the race, and a long tape showing the location and intensity and frequency of the various potential and open conflicts on various parts of the planet. Finally they were fed the old but useful analogy about the problem-child left with a matchbox in a room filled with inflammable material; and were then asked to compute from these data: first, the chances of indefinite survival for *homo sapiens*; and secondly, his probable remaining life-span.

I think that all of us imagine from time to time that we hear the computers clicking—not in outer space, but in the equally puzzling inner spaces of the human mind, with its private clocks and private calendars. For that, of course, is the space—call it the collective unconscious, if you like— where our collective destiny is being computed. However, let me revert for another moment to my allegory, for at this point it takes an unexpected turn.

The computers had finished their work; the attendant extracted the tape, looked at the figures and took it in to the boss. 'It looks rather grim,' he said, shaking his head in

sympathy. The boss did not look at the tape; instead he
dictated the following message to the planet:

'Congratulations. The results look pretty bad, but the
company can only compute statistical probabilities, and the
final outcome still depends on the individual client. We
congratulate you, as usual on these occasions, on the mere
fact that you have reached the age of maturity. Before that
turning point you were assured of your survival, regardless
of the nasty things you did. You were potentially immortal
as a race, and in this secure knowledge you could indulge in
all kinds of irresponsible behaviour. This is now changed,
though you do not realise it yet. Your survival now depends
on you and on you alone. The company can do nothing for
you. Nature can do nothing more for you. Nature nursed and
protected you before you reached maturity, even to the
extent of producing a surplus of male births to replenish your
stock depleted by wars. Now you are stronger than Nature
and entirely on your own.

'The way you celebrated your reaching maturity was not
pretty. But let it pass; there have been worse scandals in the
galaxy. The company does not judge and does not punish,
because once you are past the turning point you are your
own judge and your own executioner. At this stage, justice
works by automatic feed-back. Your race will never again
feel quite safe, just as its individual members have never felt
safe since the first of them ate the forbidden fruit of knowledge. But you need not be frightened about that; there are
compensations. By learning to live with the sober awareness
of its possible extinction, your race may derive the same
spiritual benefits which the individual derives from coming
to terms with his own mortality.

'These benefits are of course considerable. You no doubt
remember your old sage who said that philosophy is the
history of man's endeavours to come to terms with death.
And since philosophy is a Good Thing, death must be a
Good Thing—or at least awareness thereof. Take that word
death out of your vocabulary and your great works of

...e meaningless; take that awareness away and
... collapse, the pyramids vanish into the sand,
...organs become silent. You know all this, but
...in an age of anxiety and transition, you con-
...cern with death as morbid in the indignant
...Victorian prudes. You deny Thanatos as the
...:nied Eros; you shrink from the facts of death as
they shrank from the facts of life. And yet the philosophy of
man, the art of man, the dignity of man is derived from his
brave endeavours to reconcile Eros and Thanatos.

'You are entering as an adult the large family of our
clients—around half a million in your galaxy alone; I
always forget their exact figure because they come and
vanish so fast, much quicker than a single galactic rotation.
Nobody interferes with them; those who vanish are their
own executioners because they prove in the long run unfit
for existence. Those who survive flourish because they have
discovered their cosmic *raison d'être*. The rest is up to you.
All the company can do is to wish you good luck—as we
always do on these occasions.'

To come back to earth—though I do not think we have
really left it for a moment—let me conclude by a brief comparison between our present outlook and that of roughly
500 years before Hiroshima. The mediaeval universe was
like a walled-in city with firm boundaries in space and time,
a few million miles in diameter and a few thousand years in
duration. In this closed universe a well-ordered drama was
taking its course which began with the Creation and would
end when the trumpet sounded and the four horsemen
appeared in the sky. In one sense we have reverted to that
vision: we are no longer sure that *homo sapiens* will go on for
ever, and we again feel that the Last Judgment may take
place in the foreseeable future. But in another sense we have
moved away from that vision: for we know that the end of
homo sapiens would not be the end of the world, merely the
end of an episode in a drama on an incomparably larger
scale than the mediaeval scenery allowed for.

44

In other words, the necessity of getting reconciled with the idea of his possible extinction may breed a new humility, and may rid man of that biological jingoism which made him regard himself as the crown of creation. The idea that the world will go on even if mankind does not, may prove an antidote to that anxiety which has held us in its grip since the burning star fell on Hiroshima, distorted our sense of values, exposed us to various forms of blackmail, undermined our dignity and our power of decision. Schopenhauer, wrongly described as a pessimist, regarded himself as a mortal leaf on an immortal tree, a leaf to be replaced next year by another, nourished by the same sap. Gradually we shall perhaps learn that the leaves which bud into life and sail away in the autumn symbolise not only individuals but other great civilisations dotted along the vaporous branches of the expanding universe. We shall be more at peace then. But it will take some time. After all, we have only just entered the fifteenth year of the new era.

The Lion and the Ostrich

The Unreasonable Murderer*

Clarence William Ward is due to be hanged in Armley Gaol next Thursday at 9 a.m. He is aged thirty-one and officially described as a 'lorry driver's mate'—that is, the man next to the driver in the coal delivery van who hauls down the sacks of coal on his shoulders and empties them into the chute.

Ward was sentenced to death at Leeds Assizes on December 14 last for murdering eighteen-month-old Margaret Walker, the illegitimate child, by another man, of the mistress with whom he lived. At his trial he was described by Chief Inspector Byrne as a man of subnormal mentality, and Margaret as a backward child who at eighteen months could not walk, stand or crawl. Giving evidence, the mother, Miss Walker, said that Ward had 'spent hours' trying to teach Margaret to walk.

Ward said in evidence that on the day of the crime he came home tired from work and plagued by gastric ulcers; he started to repair Margaret's bed while the child kept crying; he lost his temper and shook it by using his 'full force', but was not aware of it at the time. When he realised that the child was dead, he persuaded its mother to help him bury it in a slagheap, where the body was discovered nearly twenty months later, in September 1955.

* First published under the pen-name 'Vigil' in *The Observer*, 22.1.1956. See Preface, p. X.

This humdrum tragedy may turn out to be of considerable legal significance owing to the subsequent ruling of the Court of Criminal Appeal. Ward appealed on the grounds that the Judge, Mr. Justice Pilcher, had misdirected the jury regarding the test to be applied to decide whether Ward was guilty of murder or manslaughter. The Judge had instructed the jury that the test was what a 'reasonable man would have thought or contemplated' (while committing the act); whereas Counsel for the appellant submitted that the test was 'what went on in that particular man's head at that particular moment'. There was, he submitted, no reported case and no authority for the application of the 'test of the reasonable man' in cases of this type.

The Court of Criminal Appeal dismissed the appeal on January 11. Lord Goddard, giving the judgment of the Court, endorsed the Judge's direction to the jury that the only test which could be applied in these cases was 'what would a reasonable man contemplate? If the act was one which any reasonable man must have known would cause death or grievous bodily harm, then it did amount to murder.'

Since precedent has been the basis of Common Law from time immemorial, and still is, it is to be expected that the Court's ruling against Ward will be quoted time and again in the future in cases where the vital (and deadly) distinction between murder and manslaughter is involved. The law of the realm, put into lay language, will now be on the following lines:

If A kills B in a frenzy of jealousy, or as a result of anger or nervous stress, the Judge will be justified in directing the jury to find the culprit guilty of murder and not manslaughter, because (cf. *Regina v. Ward*, January 11, 1956) 'the test must be applied to all alike and the only test which could be applied in these cases was—what would a reasonable man contemplate?'

The ruling is not an entirely new departure, because the 'test of the reasonable man' has for a long time served to assess the gravity of *provocation*. The law on this point as it presently stands says that provocation can be regarded as a mitigating circumstance, reducing murder to manslaughter, only if it is shown that the provocation not only deprived the accused person of his self-control, *but was also sufficient to deprive a 'reasonable man' of his self-control.* This means that if the accused is mentally abnormal or for some other reason abnormally susceptible to provocation, he must still be judged *as if* he were an ordinary, reasonable, average Englishman.

So much then for provocation. But Ward did not plead that he was provoked; his defence was that he had killed the baby unintentionally, i.e. without malice aforethought. His appeal was based on the submission that Mr. Justice Pilcher had 'imported', in the absence of any authority and precedent, the 'test of the reasonable man' *as a test for malice aforethought* or murderous intent. The ruling of the Court of Criminal Appeal has now sanctioned this importation.

Henceforth, it would seem that in the light of this interpretation a man can be convicted of murder if, while deprived of self-control, he commits an act which a reasonable person would have foreseen would be likely to result in death. All this will make the already ambiguous and hazy distinction between murder and manslaughter even more hazardous for the jury—and for the accused.

Some jurors will probably regard the test of the 'reasonable man' as begging the question, because murder of this type is always committed in an unreasonable state of mind. Ward, for instance, killed apparently in a state of frenzy. The reasonable man *ex hypothesi* is never in a state of frenzy. Ward was suffering from ulcers. Does the 'reasonable man' have ulcers? The issue from the common sense point of view is that at the moment when A committed the murder he was *not* a reasonable man. The issue from the Common Law point of view is that at the moment he committed the crime he *ought* to have been a reasonable man.

The law of murder, as it stand today, demands that a man

*Drinkers of Infinity*

standing trial for his life should not be judged as an individual person, but by standards of a fictitious being, of an abstract idea of rationality. It is in the name of these somewhat antiquated assumptions that Clarence William Ward is scheduled to be hanged on January 26.*

* Ward was reprieved on January 23.

The Honourable Paradox: A
Postscript to the Hanging Debate*

Future historians will probably quote the House of Commons debate of February 16, 1956, as an outstanding example of what one might call the 'honourable paradox' of man. They will be able to point out that at a time when the ultimate weapons of mass destruction were being perfected, the fate of thirteen human misfits per year unleashed 'the most emotional demonstration in the House of Commons for many years'—to quote a daily paper.

The defeated side's complaint about the 'emotionalism' which surrounds the death penalty is justified, but it applies to both camps. It indicates the depths of moral passion that were stirred up, and the awareness of the symbolic nature of the issue. Time and again the silence of a Timothy

* First published in *The Observer*, 19.2.1956.
On February 16, 1956, six months after the National Campaign for the Abolition of Capital Punishment had held its first public meeting, the House of Commons carried, by a majority of 46 in a free vote, a Resolution calling on the Government to introduce forthwith legislation for the abolition or suspension of the death penalty. This, at the time, appeared as a historic vote, as hardly anybody could foresee that another eight years would have to pass until hanging was at long last stopped—and even then only for a trial period.

Evans* drowns even the voice of a Nikita Khrushchev. It is this lack of logical proportion where moral values are concerned, this obsessive preoccupation with individual justice in a floundering world, which constitutes the 'honourable paradox', and which gives the decision of the House the dignity of a symbol.

On the rational and juridical level the debate did not reach high standards. The arguments on both sides have been repeated in the past over and again, often in a more concise and complete manner; if nothing but the scoring of points had been involved, the result would probably have been a stalemate. Some of the speeches were charmingly beside the point. On the retentionists' side—which *a priori* denies that the experience of other countries has any relevance to conditions in Britain—a former Chief Justice of India regaled the House with his memories of an uprising in Bihar in the course of which the rioters 'proceeded to strip the policemen and toast them in front of the fire'. And in what must have been one of the most unusual maiden speeches ever made in the House, a newly elected Member confessed that he had once experienced 'grave temptation to commit a murder', and that one of the facts which influenced him was 'the fear of hanging'. Speaking from the opposite side, Mr. Kenneth Younger reassured the House that the maiden speaker was 'so normal and so serious-minded a person that he must be very untypical of people who are in serious danger of committing murders'.

The speech most terrifyingly to the point was made by the only Member who had actually witnessed an execution— Mr. William Reid, a former Glasgow magistrate. Yet the sober and haunting description of the process of breaking a human neck—the reality behind the abstract debate—was delivered to a nearly empty House, which it visibly failed to

* A mentally backward, illiterate lorry driver, hanged in 1949 for allegedly murdering his child. As it was later discovered that the chief prosecution witness, Christie, had committed at least six murders in the same house, Evans' innocence is now almost universally accepted.

impress: a sign that 'emotionalism' must be clearly distinguished from both squeamishness and the lure of the morbid.

On the central issue, the protection of society, there was a very curious and psychologically interesting development in the debate. It seems that the abolitionists won their case not by forcing the right answer on their opponents but by forcing them to ask the right question. The wrong question has been debated *ad nauseam*, whether the death penalty is a deterrent from crime—which of course it is. The right question is whether it is a *unique* and *irreplaceable* deterrent. Put in this form, the problem is no longer treated as one of pure expediency, but of expediency plus morality. For the question automatically implies that if the deterrent effect of the gallows is *not* irreplaceable, then it should be replaced by a less odious penalty.

In other words, the tacitly agreed starting-point of the debate was: capital punishment is evil, but is it a necessary evil? Once the abolitionists had succeeded in establishing this as common ground, they had potentially won their case. They won it not by any clever tactics, but by establishing a climate of moral abhorrence against the death cell which put the burden of argument for its retention on their opponents.

Since Roy Calvert's classic, *Capital Punishment in the Twentieth Century*, was published in 1927, abolitionists have indefatigably collected statistical evidence to the effect that abolition did not lead anywhere to an increase in the murder rate—only to be told that this was negative evidence and that they must show proof positive that what did not happen elsewhere would not happen here. The Commons debate reversed the situation: it was a challenge to the Government to show cause why, if any country, even a country physically and morally in shambles as Germany was in 1948, could abolish the death penalty without ill-effect,

55

this country should need the continued protection of the hangman.

This shifting of the burden of proof was not the result of logical persuasion, but of a change in moral approach. Some of the new Conservative Members who tilted the balance were probably quite unaware of these dialectical subtleties; they took it for granted that capital punishment is an evil, which must go unless their leaders could prove that it must stay.

Perhaps the strongest support for the abolitionist case was given involuntarily by the Home Secretary in his opening, and by Mr. Butler in his closing, speech; and particularly in their references to the danger of judicial murder. Next to the problem of deterrence, miscarriage of justice was the most anxiously and gravely debated subject; the ghost of Timothy Evans seemed to have taken possession of the collective subconscious of the House.

Under these circumstances Major Lloyd-George's bland reiteration of the platitude about the 'scintilla of doubt', and Mr. Butler's cavalier assertion that 'no innocent man has been hanged within living memory', sounded not only hollow and unconvincing but almost shockingly irreverent. The Home Secretary also brought up the case of the three men recently released after having been wrongfully convicted of assaulting a policeman. Against the general assumption, based on classic precedents, that if the policeman had died of his injuries, the three man would have been hanged Major Lloyd-George asserted that he was 'absolutely certain' they would not have been executed, and that he would have recommended their reprieve.

It was obvious to both retentionists and abolitionists that 'absolute certainty' about a fictitious situation cannot exist in any mortal mind, and that the statement was verging on *hubris*, the sin of spiritual pride which haunts Greek tragedy. It may have reminded some wavering Members of Lafayette's 200-year-old dictum: 'I shall ask for the abolition of capital punishment until I have the infallibility of human judgement demonstrated to me.'

56

All this contributed to the outcome. But all the arguments put together do not add up to the Commons' decision: its ultimate cause was a revolt of moral conscience. Millions of words have been written on capital punishment, but when the echo of all this eloquence has died down, a small voice will perhaps be remembered—that of a Mr. Bonsall of Manchester who, in a letter to *Picture Post*, summed up in fourteen words the evil paradox of the death penalty:

'*The murderer has killed. It is wrong to kill. Let us kill the murderer.*'

Animals in Quarantine[*]

At a dinner party last year I made the half-serious remark
that somebody ought to start a crusade against our
anachronistic quarantine regulations, which are unique in
the world. This somehow found its way into the political
column of a newspaper,[†] and letters came pouring in from
the most unexpected quarters. A few were abusive: any
relaxation of the six months' confinement of dogs and cats
entering the country would lay us open to a 'flood of rabies
infection', and we would run through the streets barking and
foaming and biting each other's legs.

Most letters, however, came from people who, for professional reasons, must travel abroad: members of the
Foreign Service, members of the Forces stationed abroad,
representatives of British firms in Europe, including childless
couples and families with small children. They revealed
misery and resentment on a quite unsuspected scale. Senti-
mentality apart, a dog *is* treated in this country as an
important member of the household, and the distress caused
by its solitary confinement for six months in a more or less
nasty kind of concentration camp is considerable. Since dog
owners have no collective representation or Parliamentary

---

[*] First published in *The Observer*, 1.4.1962, under the title: 'The
Scandal of the Quarantine'.

[†] Peregrine Worsthorne's column in the *Sunday Telegraph*, 24.12.1961.

lobby, the large numbers of those victimised by this cruel and outmoded practice is not appreciated by the Government and public. But let some of these letters speak for themselves.

From Lt. Col. F. J. Burnaby-Atkins, Military Attaché, Lisbon:

> I have been a soldier for twenty-two years . . . when returning to England at the end of my tours abroad I have had to go through the agonies of deciding whether to bring my dog home, pay a huge quarantine boarding fee and finding on some occasions a changed dog at the end of the six months, or to part with the dog. Before long I shall be faced with a similar decision and this time, whatever I do, I shall provoke the misery of my four small children as well as my own.

From Sir Gerard d'Erlanger:

> Not only as a private individual have I felt for a long time that the quarantine laws were outmoded and intolerable, but also as a former Chairman of two of the world's greatest travel organisations, namely B.E.A. and B.O.A.C., I have known that our laws were a great deterrent to a number of foreigners who would otherwise visit this country, and conversely to a considerable number of U.K. subjects who would otherwise make journeys abroad.
>
> If the statistics of the World Health Organisation quoted by you are correct, and I have personally no doubts that they are, then I can but feel that the survival of our present regulations is merely one of archaic prejudice benefiting a few people who stand to profit thereby as opposed to the well-being and happiness of the majority who would benefit by their cancellation or modification.

From Sir William Hayter, Warden of New College, former Ambassador to Moscow:

> When we were in the Foreign Office it was impossible to have a dog because of the quarantine . . . I have known several cases in the past of foreign diplomats refusing to be sent to London because it meant parting with their dogs.

From a young woman:

> As a member of the Foreign Service I am, perhaps, one of those particularly affected by this obsolete ruling ... My faith was finally shattered when the Ministry informed me my two dogs *could not be kennelled together* as the whole point of quarantine was isolation! This despite the fact I had been willing to sign an undertaking to agree to both dogs being destroyed should one contract the disease.

The same idiotic separation was inflicted on the two dogs of the present American Ambassador to this country.

There were more than a hundred of these letters, and they still keep coming in, from Chile and Hong Kong and God knows where. From Burbage in Leicestershire a young man wrote that he was unable to decide whether or not to accept a six-months position abroad because of his dog. A dancer in Hammersmith had to 'refuse a very lucrative engagement in Paris because I would not leave my chihuahua for six months'. Several officers' wives wrote from abroad about 'gangs of stray dogs disconsolately wandering in British garrisons abroad, when their masters have to leave them behind, because they will not settle with new owners'. A B.O.A.C. official described how,

> all too often, fine, healthy dogs are put down because their owners cannot face putting them into quarantine ... Six months is $3\frac{1}{2}$ years in a dog's life. Certain it is that many dogs are distressed by this sudden imprisonment in solitary confinement day in and day out. Some express it by persistent howling; others by just sitting, all the spirit gone out of them. The age-old covenant between dog and man is broken.

Another correspondent reported the case of a blind American, Mr. Davis Duty, 'who came to England to study on a scholarship. His Alsatian seeing-eye dog came with him. She was taken from him when he landed and quarantined for six months. During that time his classmates had to guide him to school.'

A diplomat on home leave wrote from the Travellers

Club: 'I once had the curiosity to call in at the R.S.P.C.A. in Jermyn Street to inquire about a possible campaign against existing regulations, and was greeted by an almost hysterical vet who avowed that improvements were for all time out of the question. I thought and think this a strange attitude for a supposed scientist, but it shows the strength of feeling.'

The last quotation leads to the heart of the matter, for unfortunately that vet's attitude is typical of the attitude of many well-meaning but uninformed animal welfare bodies. It reflects the irrational terrors which the subject of rabies evokes, the aura of superstitious lore around it, and its unconscious echoes of the werewolf motif. And since the terrors of the unconscious are not allayed by statistics, few people realise that while rabies is indeed a terrible disease, it is virtually extinct and almost impossible to contract, however hard you try.

As more distress signals from frustrated dog owners kept coming in, I made it a weekend hobby to get at the facts. These are in such startling contradiction to the nonsense periodically dished out in defence of quarantine by Ministry of Agriculture spokesmen in the House that I had better name my sources. These are the reports of the World Health Organisation's (W.H.O.) Expert Committee on Rabies, and the *American Journal of Public Health*.*

Most countries allow free entry to dogs from rabies-free countries and free entry to dogs from countries where rabies still exists, provided the owners can prove that the dogs have been inoculated against rabies; a few like Sweden impose a quarantine of maximum four months on dogs from rabies-infected countries. It is clear, therefore, that other countries are taking risks which we are unwilling to face. Let us

* W.H.O. Technical Report Series, Geneva, 1950, '54, '57 and '61; W.H.O. Bulletin Vol. 10(5); *A.J.P.H.*, Vol. 45, No. 8; and W.H.O. World Survey on Rabies (not yet published), 1960–61. The Technical Report Series can be bought at H.M. Stationery Office.

examine these risks in the light of the rabies statistics for the last three years.

Of altogether nineteen European countries mentioned in the W.H.O. World Survey, there were, in 1958, human casualties in three countries. These fall into two categories: persons who had not been administered treatment ('untreated') and those who had been treated. The countries were: Yugoslavia: untreated: 6, treated: 1; Poland: untreated: 3; Italy: untreated: 1, treated 1 (these were the first cases of human rabies in Italy in forty years). Total casualties for 1958 in nineteen European countries with a total population of approximately three hundred million: 14 untreated cases, 8 treated. Casualties for 1959: untreated cases: Poland 1, Spain 2, Yugoslavia 3. Casualties among those treated: nil. Casualties for 1960: untreated: Poland 3, Spain 1. Casualties among those treated: nil.

United States, 1958: 3 deaths, caused one each by rabid skunk, bat and fox. None caused by dog. 1959: 4 untreated, 1 treated. 1960: 1 in each category.

In other words, in the last two years, in the United States and Europe together, out of a total population of some 480 million people, the number of reported deaths among treated persons was 1 in the U.S.A., nil in Europe. Human rabies in these areas is to all intents and purposes extinct. But it is still used as a bogy by the advisers of the Ministry of Agriculture, Fisheries and Food. Both human and canine rabies have been extinct, to quote a few examples, in Australia since 1867, in Denmark since 1889, in Ireland since 1903, in Holland since 1923, in Norway for 'at least a hundred and fifty years'.

England has not done quite so well, in spite of her canine Iron Curtain. Several people have died of rabies in this century, the last in 1955. Since the last case of animal rabies occurred in 1922, these people presumably contracted the disease before their arrival here.

This shows that to be really on the safe side, we ought to extend quarantine to human travellers (couples, of course, isolated from each other). Dogs are indeed much safer. They cannot be carriers of smallpox, syphilis, influenza, etc. According to the Ministry of Agriculture, the number of dogs quarantined in the last twelve years (1950–61) was 24,323, and the number of cats 3,075. How many of these 27,400 animals who served altogether 14,000 quarantine years, proved to be a potential danger to this country? *Not a single one developed rabies.*

But in these ten years, 3·4 per cent of the dogs and 14 per cent of the cats died in quarantine for other reasons—as far as cats are concerned, because of the periodic epidemics of feline influenza and enteritis, which keep occurring in these model institutions of disinterested animal welfare. These casualties apart, no statistics can reflect the miseries of the captive animals and their worried owners. Not to mention the cost, on an average £50 for a dog.

There are three reasons for the rapid disappearance of rabies in animal and man: (*a*) because, to quote Pasteur's biographer, Professor René Dubos, 'few of the human beings bitten by mad dogs ever develop rabies', (*b*) the efficacy of the improved Pasteur treatment in humans that were bitten, (*c*) the efficacy of the preventive vaccination of dogs.

Rabies is caused by a filter-passing virus which attacks the central nervous system. Unlike smallpox and other infectious diseases transmitted by any contact or through the air, rabies is only communicated to man by the saliva of the affected animal entering through a wound, or abrasion, or mucous membrane. Accordingly, the Rabies Expert Committee of W.H.O. expressly states that in the case of indirect contacts or licks on unabraded skin by a rabid dog no treatment is indicated.

Moreover, it is quite untrue that dogs can be rabies *carriers* in the sense of transmitting the disease through lick or bite, without the dog itself showing open symptoms. This further example of rabies lore is refuted by the W.H.O.

Expert Committee's conclusion: 'A biting animal should be kept under observation for a period of ten days. If the animal shows no signs of illness during this period, it can be safely assumed that the animal was non-infective at the time of biting.'

The treatment of humans bitten by rabid or suspect dogs is in fact a preventive immunisation by vaccine or serum before the disease has had time to develop (the average incubation period is between six weeks and three months). As the figures show, the protection it affords is as nearly complete as that of any treatment can ever be.

During a serious outbreak of canine rabies in Detroit—a town with a considerable Negro population reluctant to submit their dogs to preventive inoculation—the medical authorities kept check on every human being reported to have been bitten by an animal, rabid or not. The number of people bitten per year was around 8,000 in 1939, and fell by 1953 to 5,000. *Yet no human casualties have occurred since 1939*, and from 1954 onward no further cases of canine rabies were reported. Compare these facts, published by the American Health Association, with our Ministry of Agriculture's answer to a Parliamentary question *re* quarantine on 29.10.1956: 'The amount of suffering which could result from a single outbreak of rabies in a dog is very considerable indeed.'

To turn from statistics to personal experience, I had the privilege more than thirty years ago, in Novisad, Yugoslavia, to be bitten by a dog which was subsequently shot and proven rabid. The treatment consisted in twelve subcutaneous injections in the abdomen, and was about as unpleasant as a penicillin injection. All I remember is that the nurse who gave them was very pretty.

So much for the risks to humans. But what about the risks to British dogs through contact with alien dogs? The answer is preventive inoculation—practised by vets all over the world —except in England *where it is not allowed*. It consists of a single intramuscular injection in the thigh, which does not inconvenience the dog. Its efficacy has been tested both in the laboratory and in the field.

The laboratory experiments consist of vaccinating a group of dogs and then 'challenging' them a year or more later by injection with virulent rabies virus. In the first experiment reported by W.H.O., the interval betwenn vaccination and challenge was one year. None of the vaccinated dogs developed rabies. Of the non-vaccinated, control animals, 72 per cent died. In the second experiment, the interval was two years and three months. There were no deaths in the vaccinated group; 86·1 per cent of the non-vaccinated control group died.

The same vaccine (LEP Flury strain) was employed in three large field experiments. In the Detroit campaign which I mentioned, altogether 7,000 dogs were vaccinated; none of these caught rabies. In Israel, after the Arab–Jewish war of 1948, the Arabs had left thousands of stray dogs behind, and rabid jackals were rampant. Mass vaccination and the destruction of strays reduced animal rabies from 194 cases in 1949 to 3 in 1953. The Israelis, however, also used a slightly inferior, home-made vaccine, and a small, unstated number of vaccinated dogs did contract rabies. In Malaya, canine rabies in 1952 reached an all-time peak of up to forty cases a month. In January 1953, a mass canine vaccination campaign was initiated by the Government; six months later W.H.O. reports, 'the country was entirely free of rabies'. The vaccine takes full effect after four weeks; out of 90,000 dogs vaccinated, altogether three dogs developed rabies— all in the first three weeks after vaccination.

On December 3, 1953, Lord Fraser of Lonsdale (then Sir Ian Fraser) asked the Ministry of Agriculture 'whether he will consider relaxing the quarantine regulations applicable to dogs if evidence can be produced that they have been effectively inoculated?' Answer: 'No, Sir. Inoculation cannot be relied on to give complete protection against the spread of rabies.' Three years later, Sir Ian repeated the same question. Answer: 'Inoculation would not be a safe substitute for quarantine . . . Vaccinated dogs have contracted rabies on a number of occasions.'

It is significant that the last case of an imported dog developing rabies in quarantine occurred in 1949—a year or two before the reliable Flury strain vaccine became known. Since then, dog owners in other countries have their dogs vaccinated—either as a matter of routine or before travelling, because a vaccination certificate is demanded at most frontiers. This is the reason why no other rabies case has occurred for the last twelve years among the 27,398 dogs and cats quarantined for no earthly purpose on these hospitable shores.

A proposal

Superstition combined with ignorance and administrative inertia are the main reasons for the silly and cruel practice. Subsidiary factors are the breeders' flourishing export trade (amounting to about half a million pounds a year), their fear of foreign competition, and various vested interests.

I have little hope that reform will be speedier than in the case of other cherished anachronisms—such as hanging by the neck. But I do believe that a modest compromise proposal could be put into effect with a little public support. What I propose does *not* refer to the importation of domestic animals of foreign origin. It merely aims at the *exemption from quarantine of dogs (and cats) born and bred in this country, returning from abroad in their owners' care, equipped with a British veterinary surgeon's certificate of having been inoculated against the hazards of rabies not less than one month before leaving the United Kingdom and not more than two years before the date of return.*

There is an international form suggested by W.H.O. for such certificates, and identification of the animal is done by tattooing the ear.

This proposal has now the support of prominent Members of both Houses, of the Foreign Service, and of H.M. Forces. But the protective vaccination of dogs is still prohibited in this country. This in spite of the World Health Organisation's finding that vaccination provides 'excellent immunity for at least three years'; that vaccination 'does not constitute a danger for men or animals'; and its recommendation that 'as a sound public health procedure dog owners should be encouraged to have their pets vaccinated as soon as possible after they are three months of age'.

These recommendations are ignored and passed in silence whenever the subject is brought up in the House. Instead, the Ministry's spokesmen on these occasions invariably quote a single standard phrase, reiterated in every W.H.O. report as a matter of routine, that rabies-free countries should either prohibit the importation of dogs and cats altogether, or subject them to prolonged quarantine. The World Health Organisation is an ultra-conservative body—which makes its unqualified reliance on vaccination all the more authoritative; the phrase quoted is in the nature of those somewhat abstract admonitions to extreme caution—like 'always carry your gas-mask with you'—which such bodies are in duty-bound to make.

No other country adheres to it; but it has been a godsend to British Government spokesmen, and their permanent alibi. Luckily, however, it refers only to imported animals, not to animals returning to their own country, and thus does not affect our proposal that people should be allowed to have their dogs vaccinated, as they are allowed to do everywhere else, to take them abroad and bring them home again.

The risks to man and dog have been shown to be imaginary. Even in the highly unlikely case of a dog actually being bitten by a rabid jackal or dachshund in foreign lands, the World Health Organisation, for all its over-cautious attitude, has no more drastic recommendation to make than this: 'If the animal has been previously vaccinated within three years with Flury strain vaccine, revaccinate and restrain (leashing and confinement) for thirty days.'

All this may seem a rather trivial matter. But so is the withdrawal of a citizen's passport; and this is what the quarantine law amounts to for a great number of people. For others it amounts to the prohibition to keep a pet. In both cases it is a painful deprivation which cannot be justified on any conceivable grounds except stubborn prejudice; and nobody who has seen his once lively dog slowly going to pot in its solitary lock-up, and had to pay fifty-odd pounds for it, will break into cheers at the august pronouncement of the spokesman for the Ministry of Agriculture, Fisheries and Food (*Hansard*, 3.2.1953):

'After the experience of thirty years it is proved that this country is far in advance of any other country in this respect.'

Dogs, Sticks and Smugglers*

In his days as a Parliamentary reporter, Charles Dickens wrote an address on administrative reform from which the following quotation is taken:

> Ages ago a savage mode of keeping accounts on notched sticks was introduced into the Court of Exchequer and the accounts were kept much as Robinson Crusoe kept his calendar on the desert island . . . In the reign of George III an inquiry was made by some revolutionary spirit whether, pens, ink and paper, slates and pencils being in existence, this obstinate adherence to an obsolete custom ought to be continued, and whether a change ought not be effected. All the red tape in the country grew redder at the bare mention of this bold and original conception, and it took until 1826 to get these sticks abolished. In 1834 it was found that there was a considerable accumulation of them; and the question then arose, what was to be done with such worn-out, worm-eaten, rotten old bits of wood? The sticks were housed in Westminster . . . and so the order went out that they were to be privately and confidentially burned. It came to pass that they were burned in a stove in the House of Lords. The stove, over-gorged with these preposterous sticks, set fire to the panelling; the panelling set fire to the

* 'The Scandal of the Quarantine' had a rather explosive effect, as indicated in the present article, published in *The Observer* three weeks after the first, in reply to the controversy which it had aroused. (Original title: 'Dog Quarantine: A Final Word', 22.4.1962.)

House of Commons; the two houses were reduced to ashes; architects were called in to build others; and we are now in the second million of the cost thereof.

I do not mean to suggest that incensed dog owners should set fire to the Houses of Parliament. More than a thousand of them have written to *The Observer* and the Canine Defence League in support of the petition to exempt from quarantine home-bred dogs vaccinated by British vets before going abroad.

Among the signatories are soldiers and diplomats in leading positions, medical men, University professors, and such international authorities on biology as Sir Julian Huxley and Peter Scott. All of these are well aware of the fact that rabies is a terrible disease and would never advocate a measure endangering the safety of man or animal.

Less than 2 per cent of the letters received were opposed to the petition; but some of them protested against the prominence given to this issue. The Committee for the Abolition of the Death Penalty frequently receives similar complaints: why all this ado about the fate of a few wretches at a time when mass annihilation threatens us all. If this kind of argument were accepted, all protest against unjust or corrupt practices would die away. Quarantine is a relatively minor scandal, but it has gone on unchallenged for half a century, and since it has become a matter of public dispute, it was desirable to get at the facts, which had been systematically withheld from the public.

The case against the proposed reform was put before the House of Lords on April 10 by the Government spokesman, Lord Waldegrave. His main arguments were that in so far as dogs are concerned preventive vaccination 'is not completely effective'; in so far as human beings are concerned he quoted the World Health Organisation report that in 1960 'eighty-one people died during or after treatment'. Both statements are correct.

The eighty-one deaths refer to the total population of the

world (with the exception of countries in the Soviet bloc, which did not report)—a population of nearly three thousand million. The global death statistics of common diseases are compounded in units of millions, and rare diseases in units of hundreds of thousands. The figure of eighty-one deaths— nearly all of them in India, Africa and the Arab countries; not a single one in Europe—is conclusive proof that rabies in *humans* is practically extinct.

As for *canine* rabies: it still exists in some sixty countries in the world, but is rapidly vanishing everywhere, thanks to the World Health Organisation's mass-immunisation campaigns with the miraculous Flury vaccine, which came into use some ten years ago.

The risk that a home-bred dog vaccinated by a British veterinary surgeon should turn out to be the one dog in a hundred thousand on whom the vaccine does not take effect; that precisely this one freak should be bitten abroad, and that on top of it all its owner should fail to detect the unmistakable symptoms of the disease during its early period when the dog is harmless—this risk is indeed infinitesimal.

And this risk is, paradoxically, not diminished but increased by the existing quarantine regulations. Because of the deterrent effect of quarantine, quite a number of dogs are annually smuggled back into this country by their owners. I know personally, from correspondents and friends, of nine cases in one year alone; there must be many more. Some of these dogs have probably not been vaccinated since, vaccination being prohibited by our archaic regulations, most British dog owners have never heard of it.

This may seem a far-fetched argument, but it is based on fact; the last outbreak of canine rabies in this country was caused by a smuggled-in dog after World War 1. No harm was done to humans, but over 300 rabid or suspect dogs had to be destroyed because in those days preventive vaccination of dogs did not exist. The risk of a smuggled dog developing rabies is exceedingly small, but since the Ministry's argument is that we must take no chances at all, the only logical course is to vaccinate our dogs and legalise their re-entry to remove the incentive to smuggling.

These, briefly, are the reasons why most countries in the world, whose governments are quite as anxious to safeguard public security as the British Government, accept a vaccination certificate as a sufficient guarantee that a dog is safe. Around thirty countries, including most of Europe, are free of rabies, and some have been free for much longer than Britain (Denmark since 1889, Norway since 1810, etc.). Yet the spokesman of the Veterinary Association in a recent statement opposed any reform by solemnly asserting that only Great Britain and Australasia were rabies-free. He must have worked it out on tally sticks.

The Ministry of Agriculture's policy seems to be guided by ignorant and misleading pronouncements of this kind, passed on as 'expert opinion'. Since this controversy began, the 'experts' have been active spreading horror tales on radio, TV, and in the tabloid Press. To quote a single example, the Chairman of the Animal Health Trust conjured up this vision of the consequences of the proposed reform; it would mean, he said, 'putting at risk the millions of other dogs, cats, cattle, sheep, pigs, deer, wild animals, men, women and children . . . fifty million humans and about the same number of animals are running the risk of the most dreaded diseases known to man'. By these methods the discussion about a small administrative reform is removed from the plane of reasoned argument and inflated to apocalyptic dimensions.

Correspondents who asked what action they could take, are advised to write to their M.P.s.

Postscript 1968

In the same issue, *The Observer* published the following editorial comment:

Dog Sense

The controversy about rabies and quarantine provoked by Arthur Koestler's article three weeks ago has so far generated more heat than light. Considering some of the distinguished scientific names which now appear on the petition to reform the regulations, the rigid official attitude is indefensible. It looks more like the instinctive defensive response of entrenched officialdom than a reasoned case.

The two points of substance are: (1) How effective is the Flury vaccine? (2) How effective are the present quarantine regulations? There seems no doubt that a considerable number of dogs are smuggled in each year. In addition, as one correspondent pointed out, the incubation period for rabies very occasionally exceeds six months. Thus the present practice cannot be represented as 100 per cent watertight. So the question is whether the reforms proposed by Mr. Koestler would increase or decrease the risk.

As there is such flat disagreement on this subject, the Government should invite some body like the Medical Research Council to appoint an independent committee to collect evidence and hear expert witnesses. This should crystallise the argument and show what reforms would be justified.

Needless to say, nothing happened, although the cream of *Who's Who* rallied to the petition. There were debates in both Houses, but the Government refused to consider any inquiry into the possibility of reform. More than 40,000 dogs and cats have gone through quarantine since 1950. Not one of them developed rabies. The last case of dog rabies occurred in 1949, before the LEP Flury vaccine came into use. As for cats—there has never been a case of rabies in the whole history of quarantine.

When the Daydream Has to Stop*

To be born into this world as a British citizen involves neither effort nor act of choice. To become British by naturalisation involves both. But although I was naturalised many years ago, I felt rather awkward when, in *The Observer's* announcement of this series, I found myself advertised in London tube stations as a 'patriotic Briton'.

To get up my courage—and also because the episode leads straight into the subject—I must recall November 1940. After the collapse of France, I found myself stranded with thousands of others in Portugal, trying to get to England and into her Army—the last hope of Europe. The United States, still neutral at the time, kindly offered me an entry permit on their emergency quota for 'persecuted intellectuals'; the British Home Office refused to let me in.

Nevertheless, with the unlawful help of the British Consul at Lisbon, Sir Henry King, and *The Times* correspondent Walter Lucas, I managed to get on board a British transport plane. On arrival I was sent to Pentonville prison, where I did a stretch of six weeks as an illegal entrant. After that I was permitted to join the Army, more precisely, the Pioneer

* In January–February 1963, *The Observer* published a series of articles under the general heading 'What's Left for Patriotism?' The present article concluded the series (the other contributors were Kingsley Amis, Sir Hugh Foot now Lord Caradon, and the Earl of Sandwich).

Corps—the only service then open to alien volunteers—
and to 'Dig for Victory', as the posters invitingly said.
Thus Pentonville was my prep school, the Pioneer Corps my
Eton.

My company was employed on a vital defence job, and we
were of course 'too keen' as foreigners notoriously are. So we
asked our British C.O. to do away with the ritual tea-break—
which, what with downing tools, marching fifteen minutes to
the cook-hut and back, mornings and afternoons, cost nearly
two hours of our working time. The C.O. appreciated our
laudible zeal and explained that we had to have our tea-
breaks whether we liked it or not because the British Pioneer
Companies, plus the local trade unions, would raise hell if
we did not. That was about six months after Dunkerque.

While digging for victory, and later in the Ambulance
Service, I came to know intimately the lower strata of the
working classes, and found them different in several fundamental respects from workers on the Continent. Sharing the
loneliness of the long-distance runners in N.A.A.F.I. can-
teens and at the snooker table in the ambulance station, I
soon learned that the world is divided between 'Them' and
'us'. The 'T' is capitalised, the 'u' is not, because 'us' had
nothing to do with class-consciousness in the Marxian sense—
as it existed in the militant Socialist parties of Europe. Politics
hardly entered into this attitude; instead of the fierce class-
hatred which had scorched the Continent with revolutions
and civil wars, there was a kind of stale, resentful fatalism. I
learned to conform to our unwritten Rules of Life: Go slow;
it's a mug's game anyway; if you play it, you are letting your
mates down; if you seek betterment, promotion, you are
breaking ranks and will be sent to Coventry. My comrades
could be lively and full of bounce; at the working site they
moved like figures in a slow-motion film, or deep-sea divers
on the ocean-bed. The most cherished rituals of our tribal
life were the tea-and-bun breaks—serene and protracted like
a Japanese tea ceremony. Another fascinating tribal custom
was the punctuation of every sentence with four-letter words

used as adjectives, without reference to meaning, compulsive like hiccups. It was not swearing; these strings of dehydrated obscenity served as a kind of negative status symbol.

Some of my buddies came from the slums; some of them had been taught as children to use cupboard drawers for chamber-pots. The majority were a decent lot, with untapped human potentialities buried under the tribal observances. In the Libyan desert, or as rear-gunners in Flying Fortresses, they would have been magnificent. But then in the R.A.F. and among the Desert Rats, the deadly gulf was at least temporarily bridged by shared danger and hardship, by that *esprit de corps* which is patriotism in miniature; and above all by an awareness of playing a man's game instead of a mug's game. The same bloke who unhesitatingly risked his life at Alamein to 'keep Britain free' would not lift a finger at Dagenham to save Britain from bankruptcy.

The steep rise of wages, the improved conditions of housing, schools, health services during the post-war years; the advent of the TV set and the washing-machine have lent the upper strata of the working classes the external trappings of middle-class life. But the internal rift shows no sign of healing; on the contrary, it has deepened and hardened into a cold class war. The frontier between Britain's two civilisations—I almost said 'two nations'—is not hermetically closed; exceptionally gifted young people do cross the line; but for the bulk of the population the frontier persists.

One side embraces the whole complex social pyramid of the upper and middle classes with its endless intricate subdivisions, but with certain basic aspirations and values in common; a collective image of 'gracious living' which everybody tries to emulate or imitate, even at the price of making fools of themselves. The other side will have none of it. It has its back resolutely turned on 'their' style of life, standards of value, codes of behaviour. 'Competition for jobs, for promotion or privileged positions—the serious concerns of the middle-class adult, are disapproved of . . . In their own sector of society and increasingly as they get older and hardened to their class position, success must be devalued as improper, as bought by sycophancy or by cheating.'*

The British working class has become an immensely powerful, non-competitive enclave in our competitive society. It has evolved its own image—a combination of Dickens and Coronation Street, of Z-Cars, 'Saturday Night and Sunday Morning'; of 'I'm All Right, Jack' and 'The Angry Silence'—that nightmare story of one Tom Dobson, an expert welder whom his mates treat as dead because, after three wildcat strikes, he refuses to toe the line.

British social history since the end of the war differs fundamentally from that of other European countries. In the late 'forties, Italy and France, for instance, seemed on the verge of civil war, and the Communists were the strongest single party in both countries. The rising curve of prosperity led to a corresponding decline of revolutionary fervour; moreover, the trade unions split up into Socialist, Christian-Democrat and Communist unions, which turned trade union politics into a truly democratic game.

In this country class relations evolved in the opposite direction. Communist influence in the unions was negligible at the end of the war; it increased with growing prosperity and full employment; today it is the dominant factor in industrial relations, and its disruptive effects are more strongly felt in this country than anywhere else in Europe. The nation gets only episodic glimpses of the true state of its affairs and believes that these are isolated incidents; in fact, they are the result of a planned, centralised and extremely well-organised campaign. Penetration of the trade unions 'to hasten the inevitable collapse of the doomed capitalist system' has been the foremost aim of the Communist movement everywhere in the world; it has been reasserted as a programme from Lenin onward in thousands of Party brochures, Party resolutions, training courses; it is one of the cornerstones of the whole doctrine. In his cautionary tale *When the Kissing had to Stop*, Constantine FitzGibbon got hold

* Tom Burns, 'The Cold Class War', *New Statesman*, April 7, 1956.

of the wrong end of the stick. It is unthinkable that Guy Burgess and John Gollan should take over Whitehall by a political *putsch* supported by the Red Army. The real danger, if the present drift continues, is a situation patterned on the 1926 General Strike, but with more disastrous consequences.

Marxian dialectics is as much double-Dutch to the British working class as it is to the rest of the British electorate. The unofficial strikers are not Communists but unconscious tools. The rise in living standards has given the workers an increased awareness of the fact that they still live on the dark side of the moon—that they do not 'belong' to a society run by Them, whose values they repudiate. They are not anti-patriotic but a-patriotic. They feel let down not only by the Establishment but also by the Labour Party and their own trade union bosses. In 1946, it was Mr. Attlee's Socialist Government which had to call in the Army to maintain London's food supply during the unauthorised strike of the transport workers. The *Tribune* wrote at the time: 'The leaders of this mammoth union (the T.G.W.U.) were clearly out of touch with the men they were supposed to represent. They seemed to know next to nothing of the mood of their members.'

Symbolic of the prevailing mood are incidents like the following from my private 'This England' file:

> A thousand railwaymen at Eastleigh, Southampton, carriage works of British Railways stopped work for two hours yesterday because they may no longer be able to have their hair cut by railway employees, in railway time, and on railway premises (*The Times*, July 1958).

Equally typical is the monotonous series of strikes resulting from internicine quarrels beteewn rival unions: firemen against footplate men, drillers against welders, and so on. In 1956 the Merseyside dispute between joiners and metalworkers about who should drill the holes in aluminium sheets led to a strike which lasted six months and attracted national attention. It was regarded as a kind of music hall joke, an endearing quaintness of characters out of Dickens. Two years later, *The Times* reported that four hundred men had to be dismissed as redundant, eleven thousand were threatened by the same fate, that production on three vessels and a submarine had to be postponed indefinitely because the boilermakers and the drillers could not agree who was entitled 'to use five stud-welding guns designed to weld nuts and thimbles to metal plates'. It then transpired that the use of this quick and efficient method had been prevented by this dispute between the two unions for the last *twelve years*.

To be sure, strikes are no rarity on the Continent either; but in no other country has the national output been crippled on such frivolous and irresponsible grounds. In this oldest of all democracies, class relations have become more bitter, trade union politics more undemocratic than in de Gaulle's France or Adenauer's Germany. The motivation behind it is neither Communism, Socialism or enlightened self-interest; but a mood of disenchantment and cussedness. Its origins can be traced back to the period after the 'Socialist landslide' of 1945 when the Labour Party had the unique chance of breaking down the psychological class barriers —and missed it. Its 'Work and Want' posters gave the impression that the whole nation was living in a Borstal.

This is one side of the picture. It needed stressing because it is usually passed over in embarrassed silence, symptomatic of the guilt feelings of middle-class intellectuals. If I have been outspoken, it is because my sympathies are with Alan Sillitoe's heroes rather than with Evelyn Waugh's. The other side of the picture is sufficiently well known and more frankly discussed: the unimaginativeness and lack of adaptability of the British entrepreneur, the old-fashioned methods of management, the shortcomings of technological education.

The combined result of all this can be summed up in a few disconcerting figures. In the five-year period 1950–55, British exports increased by 6 per cent, those of the Common Market by 76 per cent. In the next five years, 1955–60,

British exports rose by 13 per cent, Common Market exports by 63 per cent (O.E.C.D. Report on United Kingdom, April 1962). Over the whole decade 1950–60 'no industrial nation had a slower growth of per capita output than Britain' (*Time*, October 19, 1962). Last year, for instance, the gross product of French national income increased by 6 per cent, Britain's by less than 2 per cent; and over the whole period since 1950, the growth of the national income of E.E.C. countries was twice as fast as ours. Statistics are influenced by many factors; but the total trend is unmistakable. It is reflected in some recent surveys, according to which 45 per cent to 60 per cent of young people under twenty-five would like to emigrate if they could.

In his preface to the English translation of *Das Kapital*, Engels wrote in 1886 that Marx, 'after a life-long study of the economic history and conditions of England', had been 'led to the conclusion that, at least in Europe, England is the only country where the inevitable social revolution might be effected entirely by peaceful and legal means'.

It is one of the few Marxian predictions that has come true. The continuity of tradition, and the knack of combining it with piecemeal reforms, is perhaps the most impressive feature in this country's history. The bourgeoisie, instead of stringing up the aristocrats on lamp-posts, intermarried with them and gave rise to a dynamic upper middle class. Continuity triumphed even over the decline of Empire. The declines and falls of the past were catastrophic events; for the first time in history we saw an Empire gradually dissolving with a certain dignity and grace.

But the price for avoiding bloody revolutions such as every major European country has suffered since 1789, is beginning to make itself felt. Complacency has spread like dry rot; 'keen', 'smart', 'clever' have become pejorative terms. Once upon a time England was 'the workshop of the world'; if the Persians wanted a railway engine or the Turks a tooling machine, they had to await their turn or lump it. Today, as a German industrialist remarked, 'if the Persians want to

build a railway, we give them a seven-months' delivery date
and seven years' credit; *der* British gives them a seven-years'
delivery date and seven months' credit'. Britain is only just
beginning to emerge from the delusion that she still lives in
Queen Victoria's day; sooner or later she must face her
moment of truth.

The same arrested development is reflected in the relations
between social classes. The working class insists on per-
petuating its proletarian status, while everywhere else it is in
the process of merging into the middle classes. The other half
of the nation forms a politely camouflaged caste society
with a pecking hierarchy which is a unique anachronism in
modern Europe. Englishmen take it for granted that a
person's social background can be detected by his drawls and
aitches; they are incredulous when told that in France, for
instance, regional dialects apart, the vocabulary and pro-
nunciation of the educated worker, shop-keeper or industrialist are indistinguishable. The reason is simple; the
educational system is uniform; it is based on competitive
selection; rank and wealth confer no educational advantages;
access to the two pinnacles of learning, the *Ecole Normale
Superieure* and the *Ecole Polytechnique*, is exclusively based on
the candidate's merits. These two schools produce the nation's
political and intellectual élite; and the only accent which
commands respect and even envy is the characteristic
enunciation of the *normalien*.

The first decisive step towards a true democracy is to
provide equal educational opportunities for all. This alone
would enable the nation to speak the same language—both
in the metaphorical and in the literal sense. Does that imply
that the Public School system ought to go? I am sorry to say,
yes. I am not such a fool nor such a barbarian as to underestimate what the system has done to make the nation great.
But its function is fulfilled; and unequal educational opportunities, placing privilege before merit, is the original
sin which tears a nation apart and delivers it to the rule, not
of a meritocracy but of a mediocracy.

The breaking-down of these anachronistic class barriers is, I believe, the most urgent task confronting British patriotism. It ought to be accompanied by the breaking down of the outer barriers which separate England from Europe. To go it alone is unthinkable; and 'Europe or the Commonwealth' is a spurious alternative. Geographically and historically this island belongs to Europe. Economically, Commonwealth trade is decreasing, trade with Europe increasing. Our cultural heritage comes from Europe, not from Ghana, Pakistan or Australia. Our holidays, if we can afford it, are spent in Europe, not in New Zealand. If your friends assert that the Commonwealth is more real to them than Europe, and closer to their hearts, ask them which exactly are the African and Asian countries which belong to the family; you will be surprised.

In 1940, good old John Bull alone represented Europe; today he is a European *malgré lui*, but European nevertheless. The regrettable suspension of the negotiations about British entry into the Common Market has not altered my belief in the historic necessity of a united Europe, including these European isles.

I realise that I have not explained why I love this country, why I live here, and why, though I still feel at times a stranger in Britain, I feel thoroughly British when abroad. To explain all this would have been easier and more gratifying, but out of character for an anglicised European. When all is said, one loves one's country not *because* of this or that—but rather in spite of all.

Postscript 1968

As a result of this article, *Encounter* magazine invited me to act as guest editor for a special number devoted to the state of Britain. It appeared in July 1963 under the title *Suicide of a Nation?*, and was published later in book form (Hutchinson, 1963). The cover design showed the traditional coat of arms, in which, however, the unicorn had been replaced by an ostrich; the reason for this innovation was explained in the Preface:

> A chimaera, in Greek mythology, was a monster with a lion's head, a goat's trunk, and a serpent's tail. The Englishman strikes one as a much more attractive hybrid between a lion and an ostrich. In times of emergency he rises magnificently to the occasion. In between emergencies he buries his head in the sand with the tranquil conviction that reality is a nasty word invented by foreigners. This attitude is not only soothing, but also guarantees that a new emergency will soon arise and provide a new opportunity for turning into a lion and rising magnificently to the occasion . . .

Europe, My Europe!

Reflections on a Peninsula

Address to the Royal Society of Literature, read on November 3, 1960. In the chair Cecil Day Lewis.*

A few years ago one could see all over London an advertisement for a boot polish; it showed a very old, but well-preserved pair of leather shoes, and underneath the caption: 'They are well worn, but they have worn well.' It could serve as a motto for this little continent of ours: it is well worn, but it has worn well, all things considered. I became particularly aware of this during my recent stay in Asia where I spent several months—mostly in India and Japan. To be engulfed, and at times almost drowned, in the attitudes and values of an alien spiritual climate provided an occasion to make comparisons and to see our small peninsula in a new light, from a different perspective. If I were asked to sum up in a brief formula what distinguishes Europe from the other great continents of the world, I would mention two outstanding features: unity-in-diversity in Space and continuity-through-change in Time.

This sounds rather abstract, so I shall offer you a quite concrete example for the first of these two features. You have before you a specimen of Europe born in Hungary, educated in Austria, who spent some of his most decisive years in

* I have used several passages of this text in *The Lotus and the Robot*.

France, became British by naturalisation—though alas, not by accent—and who writes his books in English. Transpose this curriculum into Asiatic terms, and you would have to imagine a person born, let us say, in Ankara, who studied in Benares and ended up as a Japanese writer. The parallel seems rather absurd, yet it does drive home not only the smallness of Europe, but above all the homogenity of its culture. Wherever you look—at art or architecture, science, trade, sport, fashions in clothes, style of living—in all walks of life the common denominators weave their fabric across territorial and national boundaries. The developments towards economic and political unity are only the most recent expresssions of a much older unity of tradition which makes it possible for a Hungarian to become an English writer, or a Scandinavian film producer to express the problems which move young people in France and Italy. Europe is the only continent among the ancient geographical divisions of the world where the ethnic mosaic forms a clearly defined and recognisable culture-pattern. And this unity-in-diversity in Space has its historic source in the second aspect which I mentioned, namely, continuity-through-change, maintained through two and half millennia of European history.

The emphasis is on both: the continuity and the change, which are complementary aspects—as, to draw a biological parallel, we find stable genes transmitted by heredity from generation to generation, as a continuous undercurrent beneath individual variety. By way of comparison: Egyptian art, for instance, displayed an amazing constancy over a couple of thousand years, and so did Hinduism as a religious philosophy; but this happened in societies that remained essentially static. Europe, on the other hand, was in almost continual ferment and change; and during the last three hundred years it has altered the natural and social environment of man as radically as if a new species had taken over our planet. Yet throughout this last explosive development and throughout earlier, equally profound changes, Europe managed to preserve a distinct and continuous identity, a historic personality, as it were.

It is a curious fact that this historic *persona*, Europe, with its distinct individual profile, emerged at the same turning-point for the human race—the sixth pre-Christian century— which also gave birth to Confucius and Lao Tse, the Buddha, the Ionian philosophers and the Pythagorean brotherhood. A March breeze seemed to blow across this planet, from China to Samos, stirring men into awareness like the breath in Adam's nostrils. But at the same time it was also the parting of the ways between the Asian and European philosophy of life, of their attitudes to the basic problems of existence. Buddhism, Taoism and Confucianism, which gave rise to the great Asiatic cultures, have certain essential features in common which are in direct opposition to Western thought. The contrast is not, as one tends to believe, between so-called Eastern spiritualism and so-called Western materialism, but between two basically different attitudes to life—so different that a contemporary German Orientalist* suggested a new word for the Eastern approach to existence: *philousia*, as opposed to Western philosophy. All the evidence, from the Upanishads and the Tao Te-Ching, to the contemporary schools of Yoga and Zen Buddhism, unmistakably indicates that Eastern thinkers are less interested in factual knowledge —in *sophia*, from which *philosophia* is derived—than in *ousia*, essential being; they are more interested in consciousness itself than in the objects of consciousness. Whether you look at India, pre-revolutionary China, or Japan, you find a basic trend of thought among the great thinkers, which rejects all sense-experience as illusion, denies that the world of objects has a reality independent from the perceiving subject, and which finds it 'exceedingly odd/that the tree/should continue to be/when there's no one around in the quad'. It is an attitude which prefers intuition to reason, fluid symbols to sharply defined concepts, thinking in images to thinking in categories, and which rejects the axioms of Western, i.e.

* William S. Haas in *The Destiny of the Mind* (London, 1956).

89

Greek, logic—such as the laws of identity, contradiction and of the excluded middle. Above all, the Eastern sage strives after self-realisation through the annihilation of the thinking and feeling self; his ideal is depersonalisation, the drowning and dissolving of individuality in the universal pool of Atma, Brahma, Nirvana—as opposed to the Western ideal of self-realisation through the unfolding of individual potentialities.

This fundamental parting of the ways seems to have occurred, as already mentioned, in the sixth century B.C. It is fascinating to note how the split is reflected in the spirit and structure of language itself. Out of the same Sanskrit root, *matr-*, emerged two key words, *maya* and *metron*. *Maya*, in Hinduism and Buddhism, is the symbol of an attitude which regards Nature as a web of illusions—the veil of *maya*; whereas *metron*, measure, regards Nature as something to be grasped, measured and mastered by the mind. Thus in the Ionian school of philosophy in the sixth century B.C., rational thought was emerging from the dream-world, the hypnagogic reveries of mythology steeped in archetypal symbols. It was the beginning of the great European adventure: the Promethean quest which, within the next two thousand years, was to transform our species more radically than the previous two hundred thousand years had done.

But at this point I must again warn you against that popular misconception which identifies the Eastern attitude with spiritualism, the Western with materialism. Materialism was one of the rival philosophies of Greece which lasted about two centuries; it was revived two thousand years later, in the eighteenth century, and is now, *as a philosophy*, on its way out. But, apart from these two episodes, religion, or at least religious awareness in one form or another, had been the dominant chord in the past of European art, philosophy, and social life.

Admittedly this past is tainted and unedifying. But Asian history has been as bloody and cruel as ours. The great Hindu epics, the *Ramayana* and *Mahabharata*, are as full of savagery and gore as the Old Testament, or the *Eddas*, or the *Niebelungen*

Saga. The *Bhagavad Gita*—the nearest Hindu equivalent to the Gospels, frequently quoted but infrequently read—is in fact an eloquent refutation of pacifism and non-violence by the Lord Krishna himself. *Ahimsa*—non-violence—was as abstract a command in Hindu philosophy as 'turning the other cheek' was in ours—until quite recent times when Gandhi's genius forged it into a modern political weapon. But even Gandhi was never an integral pacifist—he was prepared in 1940 to enter the war on our side, on condition that India was granted Independence, and in 1948, he gave his agreement to the invasion of Kashmir. Similarly, Gandhi's crusade for the Untouchables was, on his own admission, inspired not by Hinduism, but by Christianity and Tolstoyanism. Let us face it: the traditional Asian attitude to the sick and the poor is notoriously one of indifference because caste, rank, wealth and health are preordained by the laws of Karma. Hinduism and Buddhism are tolerant towards other religions but display no charity towards the individual; with Christianity just the opposite seems to be true. Thus the Messianic arrogance of the Christian crusader is matched by the arrogant detachment in the Yogi's attitude towards human suffering; and the Oriental version of tolerance without charity produced as much suffering and misery as Christian charity without tolerance.

Once more: the choice is not between spirituality and materialism, but between two different approaches to reality —one which relies on intuition, symbolic imagery and essential being—the other, on reason, conceptual thinking, logical categories. Obviously neither of the two attitudes contains the whole truth; obviously they ought to complement each other, as the principles of masculine logic and feminine intuition, the *yin* and *yang* in Taoist philosophy, are meant to complement each other.

But my point is that in the history of the great Asiatic cultures the accent remained always on one side: on the intuitive, subjective, mystical, logic-rejecting side; whereas in the history of European thought, *both* attitudes were present—alternately dominating the scene, or simultaneously competing for supremacy. Examples of this creative polarity are the Dionysian and Apollonian principles; or the Greek atomists, who saw the world in terms of matter and measure, whereas the Eleatic's view was closer to the veil of *maya*— remember Empedokles jumping into the crater of Etna in search of Nirvana; and remember those twin stars, Plato and Aristotle. Think of Augustine's other-worldly rejection of Nature, and Aquinas' rediscovery of Nature; of Schopenhauer's Eastern mysticism and Nietzsche's arrogant Western superman; of Jung's archetypes and Adler's power-complex.

Thus European thought evolved through the recurrent mating of opposites, whereas Asian thought seems to have perpetuated itself by a kind of asexual process—like budding algae detaching themselves from the parent body to become separate individuals but indistinguishable in shape. The first process reflects continuity-through-change; the second a self-perpetuating sameness.

To put it in another way, the impressive thing about the evolution of European thought, seen from the Asian perspective, is the organic integration of the various trends that went into it. The first great synthesis seems to have been achieved, towards the end of that glorious sixth pre-Christian century, by the Pythagoreans who brought together into a unified vision both contrasting attitudes: mysticism and science, music and mathematics, fluid intuition and articulate reason. The unravelling of the laws of Nature, the analysis of the harmony of the spheres, was proclaimed to be the highest form of divine worship. And this form of worship, I submit, is a specifically European discovery. There were periods in which the discovery was forgotten or denied, like a recessive gene; but it always reasserted itself. It is reflected in that wonderfully ambiguous word 'mystery'. The sober physicist is after the 'mysteries of Nature'—never suspecting, poor chap, that mysterium is a word of mystic origin, and that the motive of his quest for a unified field theory which will express gravity, electro-magnetism, and the other riddles of the universe in a single formula, has more affinities than one would think with the quest for the Orphic mysteries.

Another strain which runs through the European inheritance is a specific method of sublimating emotions and putting them to creative use—a *leitmotif* which one can follow from the ancient cult of Bacchus-Dionysius to Freud and Jung. Again I must confine myself to hints in shorthand, as it were. The ṣemi-barbaric cult of Bacchus, the raging god of sex and wine, was imported from Thrace to Greece, probably a short time before that decisive sixth century. In Greece it became 'europeanised' in the cult of Orpheus, which transformed physical intoxication into mental intoxication; the word 'orgy' no longer meant drunken revelry but religious ecstasy; and subsequently the Bacchic juice became sacramental wine and part of the Christian ritual. A similar transformation occurred in the meaning of the word *theoria* (from *thea*—spectacle, *theoris*—audience). In Orphic usage it meant a state of religious contemplation where the spectator identified himself with the suffering god. In the Pythagorean brotherhood, which adopted the Orphic cult, religious ecstasy changed into the ecstasy of intellectual discovery, and *theoria* assumed the meaning of 'theory' in the modern sense. Finally, the Bacchic rite of devouring the slain god to partake of his divine substance appears in a sublimated guise in the doctrine of transubstantiation, of partaking of the body and blood of the Saviour in Holy Communion.

One branch of the mainstream of Greek thought became united, through the Neoplatonists, with the Judeo-Christian tradition in Augustine; another, through Aristotle and St. Thomas Aquinas, led to the rise of scholasticism. But my point is that all these originally independent currents, or traditions, were not just mechanically added together to form an eclectic doctrine. It was a process of cross-fertilisation, creating variety and change, yet preserving a continuous heritage from the past. The axioms of Euclid and the Ten Commandments; Aristotle's *Categories* and the Sermon of the Mount, were assembled into a grand synthesis. It provided the link between mysticism and logic, between the poetry of St. John of the Cross and the telescopes of the Jesuit astronomers in their search for order and harmony in the universe. It is this synthesis which all other great cultures rejected—the Asian cultures by rejecting the *metron* and the reality of the outside world; the African and pre-Columban cultures by moving towards different spiritual pastures.

Greece was conquered, Alexandria burned, Rome and Byzantium collapsed, yet the continuity was sustained. The migrations injected the vitality of the barbaric tribes into the tired old races around the Mediterranean basin, but Europe did not become barbarised—it was the barbarians who became europeanised.

After the long, dark interlude, Europe was reborn by rediscovering its past—its temporarily lost Greek heritage. For several centuries, the Arabs had been the sole custodians of the treasures of Greek learning. They were the go-betweens who brought back to Europe its Greek and Alexandrine heritage, enriched by Indian and Persian additions. But their long tenure of this vast body of knowledge remained surprisingly barren; whereas as soon as it was reincorporated into the Latin culture of Europe it bore immediate and abundant fruit. The Hellenic heritage was like a skin-graft which never took on Arabic culture and wilted away, leaving hardly a trace. Yet when Europe recovered its past, it immediately started on that explosive development which led from the Renaissance to the modern age.

Continuity-through-change and unity-in-diversity are essential attributes of an evolving culture. The revolutionary Humanists of the Renaissance, and the angry puritans of the Reformation, derived their 'modern' inspirations from the ancient Hebrew and Greek texts; the French Revolution derived its symbols and titles of office from the institutions of the Roman Republic; and even the teaching of Karl Marx can be traced back to its archetypal roots in the pathos of the Old Testament prophets, the Platonic elements in Hegel, and the dialectical acrobacies of the Aristotelian schoolmen.

There is always something new under the European sun, but it is the organic novelty of new shoots on an old tree, fed by the saps of its subterranean roots.

That, briefly, seems to me the secret of Europe's unique powers of resistance and regeneration. But these can be fully appreciated only by way of comparison. In spite of Yoga and Zen, which are practised only by an insignificant minority, the people of India and Japan live today in a spiritual vacuum, more estranged from any transcendental faith than Europe. Neither Hinduism nor Buddhism were able to resist the impact of industrialisation and social reform, because neither of them had the adaptability, due to a continuous evolutionary process, which the Heleno-Christian tradition has acquired. India is the most traditionalist, Japan the most westernised country in Asia—they are opposite ends of the Asian spectrum. Its centre is occupied by the vastness of China, one of the world's oldest cultures; yet it proved even less resistant against the impact of a materialist ideology, and has become the most accomplished robot state this side of science fiction. Compared to that we have not done so badly in resisting the rape of the spirit, from the barbarian invasions to the invasions of totalitarian barbarity. They have amputated part of Europe's body; the rest has once again made, all considered, a surprising physical and moral recovery.

Ever since Europe and Asia went their different ways, the European's attitude to Asia was either that of the conqueror or that of the pilgrim, anxious to prostrate himself at the guru's feet. I went to Asia in a similar spirit and came back rather proud of being a European. It may be a parochial pride, but it is not smug, for, as a Hungarian-born, French-loving, English writer with some experience of prisons and concentration camps, one cannot help being aware of Europe's past sins and present deadly peril. And yet a detached comparison with other continents leaves one with a new confidence in and affection for our small peninsula, like a figure riding on the back of the Asian bull.

The Silent Generation*

'It is closing time in the playgrounds of the West,' Cyril
Connolly decided a few years ago; as a matter of fact, there
have never been more playgrounds on the continent of
Europe.

Swimming-pools and ski-lifts, sports stadia and tennis
courts, sailing clubs and camping sites have been springing
up everywhere in these years of the cold war; and the shiny
rash of hotels, boarding-houses, nightclubs and Espresso bars
is spreading to the last 'unspoilt' Mediterranean fishing
village and Tyrolean mountain hamlet. During the holiday
season, which has gradually expanded to two winter and
three summer months, traffic over the Brenner Pass is slower
than in Oxford Street, and large regions of the Continent,
from the Costa Brava to the blue Danube, witness an unprecedented mass-migration in search of new pastures for
play.

* First published in *The Observer*, 16.8.1959, under the title 'The Young
European of Today'. As this volume goes to press nine years later, 'Beat-
niks' and 'Teddy-boys' have gone out of date. They were superseded by
Rockers and Mods, and these in turn by the Hippies, Drop outs, Provos
and Flower People. Nevertheless, I believe that this Profile of a Silent
Generation representing the vast majority of young Europeans, in
contrast to an exhibitionist minority, was on the whole a valid
assessment at the time, and should not be distorted by hindsight (see
Postscript).

The horsemen of these migrating tribes are the young Vespa and Lambretta riders, shooting in and out of the lines of staid family vehicles, mostly in pairs, often in hordes. The social transformation of the post-war years, which made the working classes for the first time appear as holidaymakers on the stage of history, seems to be the principal cause of this upheaval; second in importance is the generation of young people, roughly half as old as the century, for whom the ski-lifts and swimming-pools, the camping sites and Espresso bars cater.

Increasingly bored with my own generation, with the mess that we made of our public and private affairs, I became more and more interested in this new generation in France, Italy, Switzerland, Germany, Austria. However different their national and social backgrounds, a general impression began gradually to take shape, a portrait of the young European of the Common Market era—rather like the picture of 'the average U.S.A. housewife' in American magazines, arrived at by the super-imposition of a thousand individual photographs.

The first thing that struck me was that the portrait bears no resemblance whatsoever to the much publicised Drum-Beatniks and Peeved Young Men (anger needs an object, peevishness does not). In the second place, it made me see the Teddy boys and juvenile delinquents, who in England monopolise the public's attention, as an overrated marginal phenomenon. It is true that they also exist on the Continent, particularly in the German-speaking countries (where they are called *Halbstarke*), and even in Poland and Russia ('hooligans' and 'tango boys'). But they are, just as their literary mouthpieces are, no more than a noisy, show-off minority whose antics have distorted the older generation's judgement of those who are preparing to take over from them.

The composite portrait shows an earnest, sober, bland face. It is uncommitted and noncommittal. Its features provide no clues to individual character and temperament, but they already bear the professional stamp of the future manager, engineer, businessman or career-woman. The girls mostly look like competent private secretaries and equally competent future mothers, whose family planning will be made dependent on the availability of baby-sitters. They are remarkably un-decadent, un-morbid, free of *Welt-schmerz*. Born into the worst century on record, they are untouched by *le mal du siècle*.

The most astonishing change has come over the French. The phosphorescent and decaying young people who appear in the pre-war novels of Julian Green, Martin du Gard, Gide, Céline and Sartre, seem to belong to a different nation and century. Sagan is idolised because she is so viciously naughty, so exotically unlike the new, healthy, outdoor generation—a hoydenish version of Oscar Wilde or Alasteir Crowley. But even she is a *grande sportive*, who impressed the lusty Vespa riders by smashing up her racing-cars.

Reckless driving seems to be the only common vice of this youth. They drink mostly fruit juices, Coca-Cola, an occasional glass of beer. This, surprisingly, applies also to France, where the sight of a young man in a bistro sipping pineapple juice through a straw would have been unimaginable before the war. The change is epitomised by the migration of the young from pubs, nightclubs and bars to the Espresso and caféteria; an all-European phenomenon which produced the Viennese quip of the 'espressionist generation'.

As for the 'sexual problem', the answer is contained in a remark overheard in a Zurich bookshop, where a girl of about twenty, pointing at a book which bore precisely that title, drily asked her companion, 'Why *problem*?' This, of course, is a little oversimplified, but not much. Sex is still a fascinating topic, but less of a problem designed for verbal intercourse. Pre-marital sex is losing its flavour as a forbidden fruit, and is considered as a more or less normal expedient while waiting for the proper flat and income to settle down. This, however, does not mean promiscuity after the pattern of the post-First World War generation. The

98

desire to settle down early is genuine, but practical considerations take precedence over romantic hurry.

'We won't marry until we can get into a three-room flat,' a German girl of twenty-one explained; she works as a typist and has been engaged for the last three years to a printing designer. 'What is the use of moving into a one-room flat if we would have to move again before the first baby arrives? We shall wait, and in the meantime continue to spend weekends together.'

A panorama of the roaring 'twenties would show young couples jazzing in close embrace in a darkened room among empty bottles and disordered sofa-cushions, the girls' skirts ending above the knees and their hair above the ears. The next generation of the 'socially conscious' 'thirties seemed to spend its time at packed protest meetings, or marching behind flags, or tensely arguing in discussion groups. The 'forties brought the war, occupation, famine, resistance, followed by the shadow of civil war. Thus each decade since 1920 produced a generation with a distinctly different profile —the libertine, the rebel, the fighter.

The generation of the 'fifties has no distinct profile. They are neither libertines nor rebels, and have no desire to fight. They are indifferent to politics, not much interested in literature and the arts, and as immune against infectious isms as we in the 'thirties were prone to them. They seem to have no ideals except getting on in their profession, forming a limited family, going on holiday in the new car. Thus this super-historical age of ours has produced a generation which seems to live outside History. Under the parabolic orbits of rockets and inter-continental missiles they have peacefully settled down to cultivate their little gardens.

The astonishing thing is that these generalisations do apply to the vast amorphous majority of the young in capitalist America as in Soviet Russia, on the continent of Europe as in Japan. (They apply perhaps less to England where the proportion of Teddy-boys is larger because occasions for fun are scarcer.) In America, the security-conscious, conformist, non-political, mass-produced young men and women are often referred to as 'the silent generation'. In Russia they are called *nibonitschjo*, an abbreviation for a sceptic who believes neither in God nor in the devil (*ni Boga ni tschjorta*), and the Soviet Press has recently started a campaign against them.

The *Literaturnaya Gazeta* describes the *Nibo* as an inconspicuous young man 'who never wears the gaudy American-type ties as the tango-boys do, nor the burglar masquerade of the hooligans'. He nearly always keeps silent. When he listens to a Party lecturer, the corners of his mouth turn down. He has nothing but contempt for the basic truths of Marxist-Leninist ideology, and all his efforts are concentrated on earning the maximum amount of money with a minimum of effort. 'Instead of devoting themselves to their patriotic duties, they only think of how to get hold of a motor-bike.'

An editorialist in the conservative *Le Monde* arrived almost verbatim at the same conclusions as the writer in the Moscow paper: 'A large section of French youth is not concerned with ideas, [the young Frenchman] wants to know nothing outside of his own world and his scooter—the only two things familiar to him.' According to a recent study of French working-class youth by Nicole Leplâtre, only 2 per cent of those interviewed professed to belong to the working classes. The majority of young workers live 'strictly enclosed by the family circle' and the class struggle is Hecuba to them.

I have collected cuttings with complaints in almost identical words from the *Yomyuri* in Tokyo, the *Times of India*, the Austro-Catholic *Furche*, and so forth. The phenomenon they describe is everywhere the same, and even the explanations point in the same direction. Thus the *Literaturnaya Gazeta* believes that the *nibonitschjo* is a product of the exaggerated personality cult of the Stalin era because 'too many too oft-repeated phrases lead to cynicism'. This is an honest admission; and *mutatis mutandis* it can also be applied to the West.

The silent generation is not deaf, but the stale slogans and anaemic values of their elders leave them cold. They know that the 'socially conscious', crusading generation of the 'thirties—the generation of their parents—was chiefly responsible for bringing about the present state of the world. They do not hate us for it, they are merely bored with us. The typical gesture of the generation without profile is a great silent shrug.

They have been labelled 'materialists'. If this is meant to indicate adherence to the philosophy which goes by that name, then the label is wrong, for they adhere to no philosophy. Above all, the categorical rejection of religion which the materialist philosophy implies is alien to them. Thus the French Institute for Public Opinion reports that more than one-half of French youth 'practises religion', and in other countries there are similar signs of a *rapprochement* to the established Churches. The movement seems to be neither very vigorous nor to go very deep; but it does indicate a yearning for something beyond the range of the headlights of the motor-bike—tempered by polite scepticism.

When all is said, to cultivate one's own little garden could indeed be their motto. It is the motto of *Candide*, at which Voltaire's hero finally arrives, having tried everything a man can try and learnt that all is vanity. These young people seem to have come in at the point where Voltaire's story ends.

Postscript, 1968

While correcting the page proofs of this volume (May 1968), students and teachers at French universities are engaged in fierce street battles with the police. It is impossible to foresee whether this new development, which took France by surprise, will blow over or whether it signals the end of the "Silent Generation" and a return to the mood of the Thirties.

101

A curious contrast to the students' revolt is provided by the results of a National Opinion Poll Survey which the *Daily Mail* published a few months ago. One of the questions put to a representative cross-section of teenagers was: 'Of all the people in the world today which person do you most admire?' The top ten of the teenagers' popularity chart came out as follows:

1. Mother. 2. The Queen. 3. Sir Francis Chichester. 4. Harold Wilson. 5. Father. 6. President Johnson. 7. Husband. 8. Elvis Presley. 9. U Thant. 10. Prince Philip and Bobby Charlton.

To the question 'How well do you get on with your parents?', 95 per cent answered Very well or Quite well. At the same time, four out of five said that their parents had no say in their choice of friends; and 54 per cent said that they would not like to lead the kind of life their parents led. Asked what they wanted most from a job, most teenagers opted for these three conditions: (1) friendly people to work with; (2) good money; (3) security. (*Daily Mail* 27.11–1.12, 1968).

Culture in Explosion

Opening address to the International Symposium on 'Art in Modern Society' at the Vienna Festival, 1960.

It seems to me that three outstanding features distinguish contemporary civilisation from others in the past: it is explosive, osmotic, and governed by feedback.

An explosion is defined in physics as 'a violent and rapid increase in pressure in a confined place'. It can be represented by a so-called exponential curve, which starts as a nearly horizontal line, then rises more and more steeply to point almost vertically upward like a snake stabbing at the sky. For the last fifty years, we have been carried along such explosive curves in all domains of life. I shall not bore you with statistics on the population explosion. They can be summed up as follows. At the beginning of the Christian era, the world population is estimated to have numbered 250 million people. It took *seventeen centuries* to double and reach five hundred million. It took *two* centuries to double again to a thousand million. Now it takes about *thirty years* to double. The situation reminds one of the Oriental legend in which the crafty sage asks the king for a single grain of wheat to be placed on the top left square of the chessboard, two grains on the next, four on the next and so on; by the time they get to the sixty-fourth square, the amount of wheat required would exceed the content of all the granaries on earth. This is precisely what faces us if the explosion continues, in about another thirty years, but probably earlier.

The increase in numbers is matched by the increase in population density. Our towns are choking. Whether you look at Tokyo, Stockholm or Rio de Janeiro, you find everywhere the same insoluble problems and the same skyscrapers sprouting upward, fighting for a place in the sun, like trees in the jungle.

The trees of knowledge form another jungle whose growth has got out of hand. The number of scientific journals all over the world was in 1700 less than ten, in 1800 a hundred, in 1850 a thousand, in 1900 ten thousand, now a hundred thousand. I could entertain you with similar figures on the exponential growth of the destructive power of our weapons; on the speed of communications; and above all on the fantastic expansion of mass culture by means of the mass media—which is our proper subject today.

Thus when I said that our civilisation is in the process of explosion, I was not speaking metaphorically. We have reached the stage where quantity changes into quality, as a liquid heated beyond a critical temperature suddenly changes into a gas. The process is reflected in our whole philosophical outlook. According to the model of the universe named after Einstein and the Abbé Lemaitre, we live in a rapidly expanding universe, whose galaxies are receding from each other like fragments of an exploding shell. The static society of the Middle Ages postulated a static universe; the ready acceptance by scholars and laymen of the Big Bang hypothesis in cosmology—though it was no more than a hypothesis—may be said to reflect our explosive state of mind. Matter has evaporated in the physicist's hands, ethics has lost its bearings, and even epistomology reflects this state of affairs. Modern logical analysis, associated with the names of Ogden, Russell, Wittgenstein and the Oxford School, has exploded the traditional methods of philosophising and the traditional systems of metaphysics; and nothing is left but the dusty semantic fallout.

The second feature that I mentioned is osmosis—the flow and resulting mixture of liquids across the porous walls that separate them. We have entered into a state of cultural osmosis. Our frontiers have become porous; native traditions are on the wane, and the movement towards a uniform, stereotyped culture-pattern, a global civilisation with a standardised style of living, has become irresistible. The same Esperanto architecture of steel, glass and concrete makes the town centres of Bangkok, Stuttgart or Melbourne almost indistinguishable from each other. The same type of furniture, dress fashions, bestsellers, films, musical hits and hairdos have made our globe more homogeneous than ever before. The peasant lads in Vorarlberg dance to the same tunes of the juke-box as the Komsomols in Sverdlovsk, and offer their girls the same refreshment in this Coca-colonised world.

For we live—and this is my third point—in a feedback culture. A feedback process is a self-regulating process. Thus, for instance, a central-heating plant may be equipped with a thermostat, which will automatically switch it off when the flat gets too hot, and switch it on when it gets too cold. The thermostat in the living-room represents the customer for whom the plant produces the heat, and like the customer it is always right. In the past, the producers of cultural values—sculptors, writers, painters, craftsmen— aimed at a relatively small audience, a small élite of customers, and tried to impose their individual vision and taste on them; but they could never be sure how their work would be received, and often had to trust posterity to do them justice. In our feedback culture, the situation is radically different. The audience is no longer an élite, privileged by birth, money or taste; it is a mass audience, embracing the globe. The decisive factor is that the previously underprivileged classes and the previously underprivileged races have both entered the stage of history as consumers of culture.

Moreover, they, the new consumers, are in the numerical majority; they control the market by their demands. They are the thermostats which regulate the output of the plant. We do not know much about how this feedback process works in detail, but we know that it involves an immensely complicated machinery of market-research, statistical evaluations, gallup-polls, and audience ratings. These enable the producers of mass culture to operate with as little risk as the insurance companies. The companies know that, by the law of averages, so many houses will be burned down and so many twins will be born next year; and the publishers of women's magazines and paperback thrillers, the producers of run-of-the-mill films and run-of-the-mill programmes on radio and TV, the designers of motor cars, housing developments and utility furniture are able to assess with a reasonable degree of accuracy what type of goods the public wants. And what the feedback indicates is that the public wants very much the same all over the world. There are, of course, regional differences, and the feedback signals are not always quite reliable, but by and large the public wants everywhere on this homogenised planet the same type of labour-saving apartments, the same three-piece suites, lampshades, curtains, movie stars, souvenirs; the same type of musicals, plastic gadgets, thrillers and comics. Already the phenomenon is taken so much for granted that we hardly notice to what astonishing degree our emotions are being prefabricated. The pinup girl, with her carefully computed bust-to-waist-to-hip ratio and facial expression is the prefabricated dream of millions of the most varied racial and individual tastes, reduced to their common denominator.

We have arrived at the crucial factor—the common denominator. The process bears the mark of inevitability. The underprivileged masses who enter the stage of history as culture-consumers inevitably have under-developed tastes. Taste discrimination, receptiveness for artistic values, the appreciation of music, require not only an inborn disposition, but also the same arduous training as the development of any other potential talent. Without such training, the taste of the majority will be determined by the lowest common denominator, and market research will feed this determinant back to the producers of cultural values. Any massive increase in the number of consumers of industrial or cultural products inevitably entails a temporary levelling down of the standards set by the former élite. Thus the combined effect of the media of mass communication, of the reduction of working hours and increase of leisure time on a global scale, could only be a sharp decline in artistic standards. The liquidation of the slums implies a period of cultural slumming. To bemoan this fact is futile; but it is equally futile to indulge in wishful thinking about 'the natural taste of the masses'. Economic exploitation inevitably entails the impoverishment of taste and style of living. Society is now paying the penalty for its past sins by having to bow to the taste of the culture-hungry masses. The hunger is there, but the palates are untrained; hence the fare that we are served.

At this point I would like to forestall a possible misunderstanding which frequently bedevils discussions of this subject. When I called the natural taste of the masses an illusion, I could almost hear the indignant protests of my arty friends, particularly at home: 'What about primitive art, tribal crafts, the potters and weavers, glass-blowers, and cabinet-makers of the pre-industrial age?' The answer is, firstly, that they do belong to the pre-industrial age, and that attempts to turn back the wheel of History are sentimental and unrealistic. In the lovely Tyrolean village where I live in the summer, no prophet of native crafts will persuade the peasants to keep on making carved and painted chests instead of buying mass-produced bedroom suites. The Indians worshipped Gandhi and carried out obediently his commands—except the one nearest to his heart: that they should discard manufactured textiles and return to homespun fabrics. Except for the very rich, they could not do it for the simple reason that the products of the textile mills were cheaper. The present Indian Government, too, is trying to revive the cottage industries, but without success. The taste for native handicrafts is vanishing everywhere. But—and this is my second point—did the masses really possess such a discriminating taste for the craftsman's products before the industrial revolution allegedly destroyed it? It is nonsense to pretend that every potter or cabinet-maker was a genius. Most of the craftsman's output was rough and clumsy—as one can see in any museum, unless one is misled by the sentimental antiquarian value which we set on it. The native arts and tribal crafts of Primitives had to go through the same long process of gradual refinement—whether we consider pottery or cave-painting—as any later form of art. Lascaux and Altamira were not spontaneous eruptions of savage genius, but the sophisticated end-products of a development which may have taken centuries or perhaps even millennia.

To return to the contemporary scene, it could be objected that I have confused cause and effect, that the mass-produced kitsch is not really what the masses want, but is forced upon them by high-powered advertising. The answer to that one is firstly that the advertising industry itself is governed by feedback, i.e. by the consumer's responses; and in the second place, that you cannot force down the consumers' throats what is unpalatable to them. The fact is they love the slush they are fed. They love it because it is adjusted by computerised feedbacks to appeal to the common denominator. You can switch the radio off when the muzak comes oozing out; but there is no denying that the majority of housewives, from Calcutta to New York, keeps it on all day. It is not the Americans who have americanised the world; we have voluntarily Coca-colonised ourselves.

Let me sum up, then. We live in a culture which is expanding at an explosive rate, while simultaneously becoming more stereotyped and uniform, and which is controlled, thermostat-like, by feedback from the new consumer masses. We have to accept these facts without illusions. The question before us is how the period of transition can be shortened, and the level of the common denominator gradually raised. To start with, we must stop regarding 'mass production' and 'mass communication' as derogatory terms. Some Scandinavian films, Ingmar Bergman's, for instance, convey an aesthetic experience as profound and moving as the *Jedermann* at the Salzburg Festival—although the former can be enjoyed by millions, the second mainly by millionaires. Wedgwood, Meissen, Delft, are, after all, *factories*—even if the word makes us blush. I mentioned that the Indians refused to go on making homespun textiles, but they have begun to manufacture beautifully printed fabrics, both in traditional and modern styles. Similar considerations apply to industrial design, from wallpaper to lampshades. Admittedly, the small irregularity in the old potter's vase, the individual touch, the personal dimension, will be missing. Well, we shall have to forsake them so that more people, who have never seen a flower in a room, shall be able to buy vases. And even mass-produced objects, from motor cars to ashtrays, can acquire a personal touch with the passage of time. It is simply untrue that a modern Norwegian glass is aesthetically inferior because it lacks the flaw of its hand-blown ancestor.

We may derive further comfort from the thought that there will always be lone geniuses who impose their vision on the public, although the feedbacks deny their right to exist. It is encouraging that such difficult and oblique poets as Eliot, Auden and Dylan Thomas, have a wide and growing appeal. In my childhood, one saw in all middle-class drawing-rooms reproductions of Böcklin's Isle of the Dead; today you see Van Goghs, Gauguins and Picassos. Literary outsiders like Kafka and Celine, Musil and Döderer, have held their own against the mediocrities. If you regard the common denominator as the flat surface of a liquid in a reservoir, then these undaunted individualists are like fountains shooting up into the air. These are as yet exceptional phenomena, but inevitably they must lead to a slow rise of the general level. Satiety of the cheap slush will help the process; with increasing time for leisure, it must come as inevitably as a child's growing out of its love of marshmallows. There has never been such a hunger for creative talent in such a vast potential audience.

In the post-war years even governments, town councils, industrial corporations and public foundations have begun to realise that culture is not a luxury, and that the taxpayer does not live by bread alone. Oddly enough, it is the small countries which are pointing the way. The Austrian Government and the Municipality of Vienna have set an example by their imaginative sponsorship of the arts. In Scandinavia, students who otherwise could not afford to go to University are automatically granted a State loan which they can repay on the never-never in later life; and the Scandinavian Airlines have cut by half the fares for students on educational holidays. On our Philistine island, we have a Third Programme which broadcasts highbrow programmes to about four million highbrow listeners every night. American students wishing to become writers, scientists, or artists, must be less than half-witted not to get a Rockefeller or Fulbright scholarship.

Cultural patronage by the Welfare State and by private foundations certainly has its dangers; it promotes conformity to established standards. But this danger seems to me small compared to the artist's dependence on the favours of a Renaissance prince, or his disenfranchisement by the totalitarian state. The combined influence of the Welfare State on the one hand and of feedback control governed by financial profit on the other, might conceivably create a healthy balance, a kind of mixed economy in the domain of culture, where planning and free competition complement each other.

You will probably think that at the beginning of my remarks I sounded too pessimistic, and too optimistic at the end. The reason is that I discussed first the present state of our affairs, and later on the potentialities inherent in it. After all, a self-regulating culture is subject to the same laws as a self-governing democracy: the people get the Government they deserve and the culture they deserve. Democracy in itself is neither lofty nor beautiful; it is just a necessity. But History seems to indicate that, to a higher degree than any other form of society, it is potentially capable of deflecting explosions into creative channels, and of coaxing the beautiful and sublime out of the common tastes of the common man.

Words and Weapons

Opening speech of the International Book Exhibition at the European Forum, Alpbach, August 1959.

When you open an exhibition of books you are expected to say some melodious things about the power of the word, or the power of mind over matter. I believe in both, and I believe that the majority among you believes in both. The point I wish to make is that the masters of our destiny do not believe in either, although they often pretend to do so.

How else could it be explained that, in an age when men travel at the speed of sound, and sounds are transmitted at the speed of light, the free circulation of words is nevertheless blocked by an invisible wall running round the globe; and how is it possible that this state of affairs should now have lasted forty years, more than the lifetime of a generation?

To blame the other side will get us nowhere. A rose is a rose, a hedgehog is a hedgehog, and a totalitarian state is a totalitarian state. The nature of a hedgehog demands that it should bristle at the world, and the nature of a totalitarian state demands that it should protect itself by a bristling curtain of censorship, broadcast-jamming stations, closed frontiers. It is further in the nature of a totalitarian state to be courageous in the face of physical threats and cowardly in the face of the only threat which it fears: the word.

The leaders of the West failed to realise this vulnerability because they set greater trust in the power of arms than in the power of words. If it were not so, the wall of silence surrounding half the world could not have survived, virtually inviolate, for forty years.

Behind that wall, for the first time in history, a complete State monopoly has been achieved, not only over the production and distribution of goods, but also over the production and distribution of ideas, opinions and emotions. This is not an accusation, it is a statement of fact. But it is also a fact that coexistence begins where suspicion ends. And suspicion can only be ended when the free circulation of words is restored.

By the nature of things, the free trade in words is in our interest and against the interest of the other side. We ought therefore to make it a part of diplomatic bargaining and be prepared to pay a price for it. Surprising as it sounds, this attempt has never been made. Our leaders bargain on questions of procedure, on questions of armament, on questions of diplomatic recognition, but psychological armaments have never been made a serious bargaining point.

If the power of the word were taken seriously by the masters of our destiny, psychological disarmament would have become a bargaining object in all negotiations, with a high priority on the political agenda, and made subject to as clearly defined clauses as other types of armament are. I do not know to what extent one would succeed and what price, in terms of political or economic concessions, one would have to pay. My point is that the method has never been seriously tried. Yet it is evident that psychological disarmament, once it started, could lead to a peaceful chain-reaction, and the reversal of the present vicious circle.

I said that to blame the other side leads nowhere; the soul-searching must start in one's own camp. By the same logic, blaming the politicians is equally futile; the blame rests on us intellectuals, who trade in words, for having failed

113

to persuade them of the power of the word. Intellectuals are sometimes good propagandists; as missionaries we have failed.

In the beginning was the word. Then the word became flesh. Later the flesh denied the word. Who is going to have the last word? It depends on the spokesmen of the word.

A Love Affair with Norway*

All nations are mad, but the Norwegians are more mad than others, and in more endearing ways. The madness starts with the geography of a country which looks like a wrinkled sausage stretched to a length of 1,100 miles, but is only four miles across where it is narrowest.

It continues with a freak climate: the Lofoten Islands, north of the Arctic Circle, have a January temperature forty degrees Fahrenheit higher than any corresponding place on earth, and Oslo, latitude 60°, has a hotter July than San Francisco, latitude 38°. The milky nights in the summer and the short days in winter are constantly evoked by Norwegians as an excuse for their supposedly difficult temperament, for they like to dramatise themselves as a people given to extreme changes of mood between exuberance and brooding, a cross between Hamlet and Gargantua.

I do not know whether this traditional image that Norwegians have formed of themselves is any more justified than the Frenchman's idea of himself as a paragon of Cartesian lucidity; but I have certainly seen them go wild with the arrival of spring, which happened to coincide with my arrival in Oslo. The leading afternoon paper came out with a streamer across the whole front page: 'SUMMER!—SUMMER!—SUMMER!—SUMMER!—SUMMER!' The town was taken over by

* First published in *The Observer*, June–July, 1960.

amorous students walking hand in hand, eating shrimps from paperbags, basking in cafés and parks, and drinking sunlight as convalescents sip broth after a long illness.

Snow and salt-water worship is the first and foremost Norwegian madness; they do not *like* ski-ing and sailing—they live for it; and apparently they have always done so. Near the famous Holmenkollen ski-jump there is a museum containing a ski that dates from the fifth century B.C. In another museum one can admire three miraculously preserved Viking ships, dating from the ninth century when, as one guide book says, 'joining a Viking raid (to Paris or North Africa) became practically a national craze'.

Even crazier is the original Kon-Tiki raft, exhibited next door. Neither the book nor the film were able to convey an idea of the fragility and ramshackleness of those rough balsa logs held together by strings like a Heath Robinson contraption—nor of the lunacy of Heyerdahl and his friends who drifted across 4,500 miles of Pacific Ocean on this floating coffin lid.

Talking of museums—the Norwegians, perhaps because they have lived for so long under foreign rule, are an extremely history-conscious people. Their museums are not concerned with displaying dead objects, but life as it was lived in the past. Thus the so-called Folk Museum in Oslo is in reality a small town containing a hundred and fifty wooden buildings dating from between the twelfth and eighteenth centuries, which were dismantled at their original sites hundreds of miles away, transported to Oslo, and reassembled, complete with their furnishings and household ware. Bergen has a similar park.

The Norwegians' working day ends at 4 p.m.; then they have dinner, the main meal of the day, and from 5 p.m. they enjoy six or seven hours of solid leisure. The young often go out sailing or fishing all night, to revel in the unearthly colours, then sleep all day. The virtual absence of darkness for several months alters the whole biological rhythm. Sleep becomes difficult, particularly when one is young, and the beginning of mid-summer madness coincides with the end of term in May.

Even when travelling by air, Norwegians have the strange habit of looking out of the window instead of reading a newspaper. Yet they travel a lot by air, because most of the country consists of barren mountains, because the distances are so vast, and there are so few people to fill them— 3,500,000 strung out over 1,100 miles.

The small S.A.S. planes hopping across from Oslo to Stavanger or Trondheim have a curiously intimate atmosphere. In Bergen we were out on the runway, the engines had been revved up and we started on the take-off run, then stopped again. After a few seconds a voice came over the loudspeaker: 'This is your skipper speaking. Ladies and gentlemen, I must apologise for a few minutes' delay, caused by a basketful of lobsters which has just arrived at the airport to be flown to Hamburg. It won't be long, the lobsters are just arriving on the runway.'

The second major national madness is art, or rather ART. Its clinical symptoms are typically displayed in what one might call the Vigeland Saga. Adolf Gustaf Vigeland (1869–1943) was, at the turn of the century, Norway's leading sculptor—a Nordic Rodin, but with a leaning towards the violent and fantastic.

In 1906 he exhibited in Oslo a one-fifth scale model of a huge bronze fountain. A public subscription promptly provided the necessary funds for the fountain, and Vigeland set to work. Eight years later, at the outbreak of the First World War, the project had grown to unprecedented proportions— apart from the fountain itself, whose bowl was held up by six giants, it now embraced some eighty monumental groups and reliefs in bronze. All these were stored in the artist's workshop—the size of an aeroplane hangar—and hidden from the public eye.

Another ten years passed, and the hangar was spawning more bronze and granite—because Vigeland had by now conceived the idea of an open-air sculpture park, near the heart of Oslo, of approximately a hundred acres covered by several hundred groups, all granite and bronze, all executed by himself. It was to be the most colossal one-man show ever seen, and it was to last for eternity. And since the Norwegians are mad, they enthusiastically agreed to the project. A committee of four experts was appointed to visit periodically the master's workshop, but no other mortal was allowed to see the Work in Progress—until the day when all would be ready.

Vigeland worked through two World Wars, and died in 1943, aged seventy-four, having spent some forty years on the Project. The work was, according to his ideas, still unfinished, but there was enough of it to cover seventy-five acres of the site reserved for him since 1924. By 1945 every-thing was in place, and the Vigeland Sculpture Park was thrown open to the astonished citizens of Oslo. That was fifteen years ago; but the controversy over it is still raging.

The park covers, I repeat, seventy-five acres, and its main alley is half a mile long. Along it are ranged 150 groups comprising nearly 1,000 individual figures of nude males, females, children, skeletons, giant reptiles and other symbolic creatures, fighting, loving, dying, hoping, despairing, most of them in frozen violent motion. The climax is a granite obelisk sixty feet high, reached by circular stairs, displaying 125 nudes struggling towards the top, trampling the dead and dying underfoot; from a distance, they look like blind maggots writhing towards the light. It is asserted that at least once a week a visiting tourist is physically sick at the foot of the obelisk.

The total effect of the park is one of genius triumphant in some of the groups of Vigeland's late period which, isolated from the rest, would be considered masterpieces—and of insanity reflected in the presumption of covering that immense area with repetitive variations of one man's vision of Human Destiny. A curious aspect of that vision, which one cannot leave unmentioned, is Vigeland's super-realistic treatment of the masculine anatomy; since all his figures are

118

larger than life, the visitor is made to walk for half a mile between two intermittent rows of outsized male genitals. This has a singularly depressing effect on both sexes— particularly since Vigeland made a special point of making his old men more favoured by nature than the young, which gives his work a distinctly paranoiac touch.

After an hour in the park, one hurries through the huge wrought-iron gates, covered with struggling giant-lizards, with the impression of emerging from a colossal mid-summer nightmare. Yet it comes to rest in one's memory as an unforgettable experience of madness on a majestic scale, and it deepens one's affection for a nation so crazy about ART that it made its realisation possible.

Another experiment in grandeur is the *Radhuset*, Oslo's new Town Hall. Its two monumental towers, dominating the fjord, are visible for miles around and look like a cubist version of Salisbury Cathedral combined with the crematorium of Golders Green. It contains the largest clock in Europe (twenty-eight feet in diameter), the largest painting in the world (eighty-five feet by forty-three of Sorensen's 'The People at Work and Play'), and its marbled and frescoed reception hall looks big enough to contain the whole Basilica of St. Peter's.

The quality of the giant frescoes, mostly executed in the socialist-realist style, is controversial; the enthusiasm that went into the building is not. Norwegians talking about their *Radhuset* are apt to remark with a self-deprecating shrug: 'We are the smallest of the historic nations of Europe, so naturally we had to build the biggest City Hall. Its size is the measure of our inferiority complex—*ja-ja-ja-ja-ja*.' This ejaculation, accompanied by a mournful sigh, is the Norse equivalent of 'All is vanity'. But what an admirable form of vanity it was to build a town hall with two huge towers and to turn them into studios for the artists who painted the frescoes—rent-free to the end of their lives. Public patronage of the arts could hardly reach greater heights—210 feet above the fjord.

Nor can the writers complain. They do not live in the *Radhuset's* ivory towers; but my Norwegian publisher, Harald Grieg, a great-nephew of the composer, has just announced a prize of £1,000 for the best first novel of the year. An English publishing firm has recently announced a similar award of half that amount. Norway has a population of 3,500,000. Great Britain has fourteen times more; the ratio of generosity thus works out at twenty-eight to one. As for book sales, the ratio of Norway to Britain is somewhere between ten to one and fifteen to one. The honours for this achievement should probably be awarded in equal proportion to the long Arctic nights, the Welfare State which provides the leisure time, and the Norwegian character.

Next to artists and writers, the most privileged group in Norway are the students. The Students' Associations in Oslo, Bergen and Trondheim are not only rich—with clubs—and boat-houses, blocks of flats and so forth—but also respected and influential. I had the privilege of being their guest on a Scandinavian lecture tour—other recent guests included the Soviet Deputy Premier Mikoyan, Ilya Ehrenburg, Sholokov, and J. B. Priestley. The atmosphere in Oslo was rather awe-inspiring—an over-crowded hall in which some 800 students sat about helter-skelter, clutching their beer-mugs. But the audience proved to be both appreciative and discriminating—at least they did not boo me, whereas they booed Ehrenburg (on Pasternak) and Mikoyan (on Hungary). After the lecture, the visitor is invited to a *nachspiel*, where the discussion is continued in a smaller circle over food and a series of drinks, starting with aquavit and beer, and usually followed by claret, sweet sherry, brandy and whisky, in that order; it may last into the small hours. One of the highest distinctions in Norway is to be decorated with the Order of the Pig—the badge of the Oslo Students' Association. Mr. Lange, the present Foreign Minister, is said to have refused all decorations except the Order of the Pig.

Yet for all their *joie de vivre* they are a hard-working lot. The distinction between aesthetes and athletes is completely unknown, together with any other form of snobbery. Since the number of students is rapidly increasing, competition is becoming rather tough, and a good many take up a money-earning profession with a minor degree, then return to their university for a higher degree in their thirties.

A specific feature of Scandinavian universities is the high percentage of married students. In Sweden it is 25 per cent; in Norway somewhat less. Sex is traditionally regarded as a healthy outdoor game, second only in popularity to ski-ing, and equally devoid of any utilitarian purpose; but most of the Norwegian students marry early, either for the sake of convenience or, frequently, because a baby is on the way.

All this may sound a shade too idyllic, and I myself thought so; so I began to look for the skeletons in the clean-smelling, gaily painted, pine cupboards. 'What are the principal problems of Norway?' I kept asking my student hosts, who handed me on from one university to the next like a registered suitcase which must never be let out of sight.

Those among them who supported the Conservative or Liberal opposition parties would express mild anxiety about the tendencies inherent in the Welfare State: high taxation, etatism, de-personalisation, slackening of the individual moral fibre. But they quite readily admitted that if the opposition came to power they would have to pursue essentially the same policy both in foreign and domestic affairs. The Norwegian Labour Party never subscribed to the dogma of Nationalisation. The Labour Government fosters private initiative, regulated indirectly but effectively by import controls and price controls. Above all, by means of a national Budget (as distinct from the ordinary fiscal Budget) the Government assures that 28 per cent of the national income is invested in long-term development projects (as compared with 12 per cent in an old country like Great Britain and 22 per cent in a young country like Canada). Socialism versus Capitalism has become a more or less hollow battlecry in most countries of the West; in Norway it has lost all meaning.

The decline of politics is made smoother by a specifically Norwegian peculiarity: the absence of class distinctions. Norway has no aristocracy, nobility, gentry or upper-middle class, either officially or unofficially. During the long centuries of Danish rule, the great feudal families became extinct, and the titles awarded by the Danish kings (all in all, three baronies and a score of lesser distinctions) were abolished when Norway became free of Danish rule in 1814. As a result, though all men are equal, Norwegians are more equal than others.

Unlike Americans, who compensate their lack of a native aristocracy by matrimonial imports, Norway is incredibly and blissfully free from social snobbery in any form whatsoever—which may be one of the reasons why Mr. Evelyn Waugh took such a violent dislike to the country. The nearest approach to an upper crust are the big shipowners, but they are democratic in their habits and philanthropists by tradition—more like the Parsees of Bombay than the finance aristocracy of the West.

Nevertheless, I went on asking my student hosts: 'What are Norway's problems? There must be some. What about Teddy boys?' In Bergen and Trondheim there were none, in Oslo there are a few, and juvenile delinquency has increased, but the rate of increase is 50 per cent less than in other Scandinavian countries. The same goes for alcoholism and suicide; and homosexuality is still a rare curiosity. Criminality—in spite of the touching Scandinavian habit of allowing convicts to spend weekends with their families—is almost negligible.

For the last time, then, what are the problems of Norway? As I said, most of my informants were worried about the Welfare State. 'It makes the people complacent. Too much leisure. We have become a lazy nation; nobody works hard enough.' But in Sweden they said just the opposite: 'We all work too hard; we are becoming robots with ulcers.' Which tends to prove that even within very similar social-economic frameworks, psychological factors may make all the difference, not only on the individual, but also on the national scale.

Bored by my persistent questions, one student burst out: 'The problem of Norway is that there are no problems.' But even that is not true. About once every year there is some violent controversy which rages in the Press and public for months on end. Two years ago there was the case of Mykle's *The Song of the Red Ruby*—Norway's *Lady Chatterley*, only more so. More recently there was the case of a certain bishop who asserted the physical reality of Hell, which caused a general outburst of indignation. Then there is the quarrel about the admissibility of women preachers. So Norway has Problems after all.

Speaking for myself, the problem that puzzled me was to find some explanation why this most thinly populated country in Europe should exhibit, within a single century, the greatest density of genius (the same question applies to another very small country, Hungary). To mention literature alone, they produced Bjørnson, Hamsun, Undset—three Nobel Prize winners out of a population smaller than Switzerland's —as well as Ibsen. Toynbee's Challenge and Response? That might account for the explorers—Amundsen, Nansen, Sverdrup, Heyerdahl; but what kind of challenge made these seafarers produce the best contemporary designs in pottery and glassware?

And why has Bergen, so close to the Arctic Circle, the atmosphere of a fishing port in Provence? And why are these Nordic civilisations of Lutheran Evangelists less inhibited in matters sexual than the Latins on the Mediterranean shores? Will anthropology, social science, psychology or what have you, ever provide a clue to questions of this nature? Or even to the question why, if you go by ferry in Oslo fjord from Bygdöynes to Bygdöy, you pay a fare of three kronen, but if you go from Bygdöy to Bygdöynes, you pay nothing at all?

I liked that ferry-boat very much indeed. It used to take me from Bygdöy, where I stayed with the hospitable Griegs, to the centre of the town, and back through the white night

Drinkers of Infinity

of the fjord; the ticket collector was a Walkyrie in blue slacks
who studied mathematics at the university. I liked going to
the movies by ferry, and I particularly liked the approach to
the harbour, where the royal yacht, the nation's gift to their
elected King Haakon, was moored, gleaming but tiny,
symbolically dwarfed by the massive town hall—from whose
towers the privileged fresco painters were probably looking
down, with a nude model in the background, thoughtfully
chewing a *Smörgasbrodet*.

Drifting on a River[*]

Last year, when I graduated from lower-middle to middle-middle age, I became addicted to a new hobby; at a loss for an adequate English expression, I shall call it *le canotage gastronomique*. The idea is to travel, in a canoe, down one of the great rivers of France—the Dordogne or the Loire; to spend one's days on the water and one's nights at a comfortable hotel; to combine the virtuous satisfaction of a sporting achievement with a guilt-free guzzle in the evening.

You travel at the average rate of twenty miles a day, paddling or drifting with the current, eating your picnic lunch on an island or anchored in midstream. A river is a world of its own: often you do not see a human being or a house for several hours; a few miles from bustling towns like Orléans or Bergerac you are in a sunny, silent wilderness where a dog's bark is an event and the rustling of the current

* First published in *The Observer*, August 1957.

125

against a dead branch sounds like the Niagara Falls. After a fortnight of this dreamy paddle-drift-and-wading progress, you discover that you have travelled more than half the width of France.

It is much more easily done than it sounds. The technique of paddling a canoe is childishly simple and can be learnt by any fool of any age in an hour. You can use a rigid (Canadian) canoe, which is transported on a rack on the top of the car; or a kayak with collapsible frame and rubberised skin, which, when dismantled, is stowed into two bags weighing thirty-five pounds each.

I prefer the Canadian because its single-paddle action is more peaceful; but since I have an open car without a roof, I use a kayak. She is nearly eighteen feet long, two and a half feet wide, very streamlined, and as frail in appearance as she is sturdy in fact, with a carrying capacity of eight hundred pounds and sufficient storage space under the canvas cover fore and aft to carry all the clothes that two people need for a fortnight, and also a folding trolley for portaging the canoe, and the books which will remain unread. She is of British make, costs around £35, and answers to the name of *Blue Arrow*.

Last summer, with a friend who plays second paddle and shall be called Crew, I travelled down the Dordogne from Beaulieu to Trémolat, and a stretch of its tributary, the Vézère. This year we went down the wine-and-château regions of the Loire, from Nevers to Saumur, some 250 miles in all.

My log of this summer's expedition starts on Thursday, June 13, in Nevers. We had arrived from Paris late the previous night, and spent Thursday morning re-packing our river wardrobe into an assortment of waterproof bags, putting *Blue Arrow* together on a grassy patch near a riverside inn, finding a garage where the car would remain for the next fortnight or so, and buying our first picnic lunch. Then, at long last, the moment arrived to fix the pennant with the red ensign on the stern and to push off, bottom grinding across the gravel, into the sudden swift current, as if stepping on to a liquid escalator belt.

The sky was cloudy and the grey river seemed incredibly vast. The last few days the papers had been full of storms and inundations in the Alps and the Massif Central, of bridges carried away and villages evacuated. As a result, the Loire had risen considerably: in places to a width of half a mile across, and even more where it is broken up by islands. The high water actually proved a blessing by saving portages over shallows, and carrying us safely over submerged obstacles; but during the first hour we felt overwhelmed and subdued.

The Loire is the longest river in France—over a thousand kilometres—and flows through the heart of the country, the Bourbonais and Nivernais, the Orleannais and Berri, Anjou and Touraine. The river was navigable up to the beginning of the nineteenth century, but the vast deforestations along its upper reaches and tributaries put an end to that; in times of drought it is reduced to thin trickles among the sandbanks, though it remains canoeable even then. The dying out of navigation made the busy water-road revert to its original nature of a liquid path through unspoiled country and often through a wilderness, with no houses, villas or towns for miles on end; even the villages mostly turn their backs on the river.

The log of the first day reads:

Thursday, June 13, Nevers-La Charité, 35 km., seven hours. Left Nevers 12.40 p.m. from 'Le Chalet du Viaduc' after railway bridge. Lunched anchored on lone beach facing the mouth of the Allier on andouillettes de vire (chitterling stuffed with sausage meat which looks in cross-section like mottled quartz), goat cheese and peaches. On reconnoitring the bridge at Fourchambault ran into a fisherman who told us the bridge was easy to pass, but said nothing about a dredge-cable spanning half the river immediately behind the bridge. Reconnoitre, always reconnoitre. Good strong current, but nasty head-wind. Cloudy all day, cleared up after 6 p.m., wind dropped, golden evening. Reconnoitred from island before entering La Charité.

127

Met another fisherman with dog on island. Lost my glasses in island sands. Moored at La Charité 7.45, washed out and shaky with fatigue (muscles not yet broken in); bath and simple dinner on hotel terrace: river lobster in Pouilly; ham with cream sauce, Chavignol goat cheese. Wines: Pouilly Fumé 1956, Pouilly Fumé Loges 1952.

'Reconnoitring' is at the same time a necessity, a ritual, and one of the principal joys of canoeing. When you approach anything in the river that looks tricky—a bridge, a weir, rapids or shallows—you can neither stop in the current nor get a proper view, crouched on the bottom of the canoe; you have to land on the nearest shore or island, and reconnoitre. This may involve scrambling up the river bank through thistles and thorns, or wading through mud, but it provides one with an excuse to stretch one's legs, smoke a cigarette, compare the cool breeze of the river with the sudden baking heat of the shore, and explore a stretch of lonely rural hinterland on which, one feels, no white man has set foot before. The church spire of the nearest village, some kilometres away, looks like a desert mirage; the only reality is the river, the cornfields with cracked soil like an old peasant's skin, meadows blushing with poppies, a white cow or goat on the other bank, and the silence. This, one realises with a sudden shock, is essential France, a landscape written in basic French, glimpsed through the back door of a deserted waterway.

Friday, June 14, La Charité-Pouilly s/Loire. M. Maréchal, a super-efficient optician in this mediaeval market town, built helter-skelter round a Benedictine abbey, produced a new pair of glasses within a couple of hours. We left at midday in blazing sun, revisited Lost-Glasses-Island, which, owing to a further rise in the water-level overnight, had an entirely different shape; this river has changed its contours every day since the Creation.

Downstream from La Charité the Loire branches out into a vast labyrinth of islands and waterways, impersonating the Mississippi. In places it spans a mile, but is broken up by half-submerged clusters of trees, islands with golden sandy beaches, and odd little *tourbillons*, suddenly appearing where a salmon-trout, disturbed in its mudbath, has caused a minor landslide in the river bed. Silver beeches dotted all round the vast horizon, suddenly reflecting an eighteenth-century Flemish landscape with only the frame missing.

Since it is impossible to know which branch to follow in this liquid maze, we left the decision to the current, which usually carries you to the deepest channel, but occasionally runs you aground on sand or gravel. This means wading and pushing, until suddenly you are in deep water again, racing down on the moving belt at a speed which feels like an express train, and which we have timed at exactly four miles an hour.

On this second day we were getting to know the personality of this river, its cross-currents and idiosyncrasies, as we learnt to know last year the Dordogne. Once, guided by the froth on the current, we let it carry us into an inlet hidden in a clump of trees, and emerged into a secret waterway which made us feel we were on the *African Queen* and watch out for monkeys and natives with arrows. Ate our sausage and cheese on an enchanted island with a small patch of yellow sandy beach enclosed by woods. Saw not a single house or person till Pouilly. Drifted through the sun-drenched silence, watched only by some statuesque, cream-coloured cows, dying to know who we were; and the cuckoos calling each other across the river to signal by jungle telegraph our approach.

We were now in the Pouilly-Sancerre country. The Pouilly Fumé is our favourite among all the white wines of France, and on six successive evenings, from Nevers to Orléans, we compared and tried to memorise the striking differences between the five available years, '52 to '56, and the two distinct grapes, the Chasselas and the Sauvignon. (The same Sauvignon grape also produces the Château Yquem.) This week of sampling, on the spot, unadulterated, the produce of a single small region, showed again how utterly silly, in these days, all claims of connoisseurship are unless coming from a member of the trade.

I shall not go into detail about food and wine, though it was one of the leitmotifs of the trip. On the Continent, food and wine are the business of the restaurateurs; in England of the littérateurs. There is something almost pornographic—the obscenity of the *voyeur*—in the prose of our *gourmets de lettres*. Instead, here is some general advice for future gastro-canoeists.

First, no wine during the day on the river. It does not hurt, but it is lazy-making and spoils the expectations of the evening. Very light picnic lunch—sausage, cheese, Vichy water: it saves both appetite and money for dinner. At the blessed moment of arrival in the evening, avoid the temptation of cocktails, Pernod or apéritif, and start straight away on a cool bottle of white or *rosé* before dinner. The difference in enjoyment, mood and staying power is amazing. Crew and I sometimes drank a bottle before dinner and two more in the course of it, without ill-effect: the Loire wine departs as gracefully as it greets one.

Try a meal with white wine throughout, no red: the Pouilly Fumé, especially, goes with everything except red meat, and particularly well with goat cheese. (The red Loire wines are rather indifferent.) Beware of liqueur. The *marc* and *prune* of the region are sheer fire-water: one glass with the coffee will do for the sagacious canoeist. Lastly, never carry moderation to excess: occasional excess proves moderation in moderation. Amen.

To illustrate my various points: at a restaurant in Langeais where we dined, the teachers of the *Lycée* of Tours were having their annual close-of-term banquet. Here is their menu. Please bear in mind that the gathering was not one of university dons, but of schoolmasters in a provincial grammar school:

Terrine Maison à la gelée
Brochet de Loire au beurre blanc
Champignon à la crème
Canard Nantais
aux
Petit Pois

Salade
Fromages assortis
Omelette Surprise
Sablés Maison
Corbeille de Fruits

VINS

Touraine blanc—Touraine rouge
(throughout the meal)
Montlouis sec (with the Brochet)
Chinon 1954 (with the Champignons)
St.-Nicolas-de-Bourgueil 1953
(with the Canard)
Côteaux-du-Layon 1953
(with the Omelette)

Q.E.D.

The first half of the journey, from Nevers to Orléans, took exactly a week. After the second day we were broken in and could go on paddling mechanically for an hour without effort, and without even being aware of it—I suppose that is how galley slaves survived to old age. But at least half the time we drifted, with an occasional lazy stroke to keep the canoe's head downstream. We developed a craze for discovering secret inlets which start as an improbable trickle in a wall of foliage, and, when you have forced your way through the scratchy branches, rewardingly broaden out into a secret channel in the wilderness. There was a great display of what we took to be rare birds, and at times the salmon rose round the canoe like popcorn—sensing, I am sure, that we were obstinate non-anglers and non-watchers of birds.

Until midday we usually travelled in a blaze of sun which must have burnt a hole to get through the hard blue sky of the Loire. It charged our bodies, like batteries, with the volts and amps needed to last through the next English winter. In the early afternoon there usually appeared one or two very small white clouds, angelic in appearance, which had the knack of turning black and spawning all over the sky before you could say a knot and two fathoms. First the river's colour turned to pewter; then came the lightning—sheet, fork and knife, followed by the sudden crack and the Homeric tummy-rumbling of the gods.

This was the signal for lengthy arguments between pessimistic Crew and my science-minded self as to which way the storm was heading and whether to land at the next village for shelter. Actually we were caught only once, just before landing. Another time we watched, near Sancerre, rockets being shot from the vineyards into the clouds; they are supposed to prevent hail. After these spectacular thunder-storms which the heat-wave brought in its wake, it was a joy to paddle through the gentle rain. Where the rain-drops hit the water they made little white crosses standing on the bubbles, like a gay cemetery for leprechauns who can always get out on leave when the sun comes through.

As for dramatic incidents, there was none. Everybody warned us against the treacherous quicksands of the Loire, and we were careful always to hang on to the canoe while wading, but never sank deeper than our ankles. Once, pass-ing under the bridge of Châtillon, the back-wash, or 'counter-current', whirled us round and drove us head on into a group of anglers on a grass patch at the foot of a pillar. It was merely funny, but a warning to be more careful about bridges. We twice portaged the canoe around bridges where the current looked nasty: at Gien and at Orléans—though more out of cowardice than real necessity. Generally speak-ing, the only dangers on the Loire are man-made: dredges with steel cables, derelict weirs, bridges destroyed in the war, and bridges in general. Without them the canoe would happily swim down with the current, like a cork, from the Massif Central to the sea.

When we got to Orléans we profited from a couple of rainy

days to return by train to Nevers, where we had left the car, and drove her down to Orléans, where we garaged her for the remaining half of the journey. It is a good idea to divide, in this manner, the trip into halves: after a week's canoeing, a day in train and car is a wonderful change. Since the river is a one-way street, the canoeist is obliged to travel through the same stretch of country three times: paddling downstream, upstream by train, and downstream again by car, each time seeing it from a different angle. On the river you sweated *pour la gloire*; on the train you relax and marvel at the speed; in the car you become a sightseeing tourist, but with that difference which familiarity with a region brings to the perception of its art. A château on the Loire, visited during a short stop in passing, is like a quotation out of context.

The remaining half of the journey through the classic château country—Orléans, Beaugency, Blois, Chaumont, Amboise, Vouvray, Tours, Langeais, Bourgeuil, Saumur— lasted another week. It was peak tourist season in one of the most tourist-haunted regions of the world, but all along the Royal Valley we had the river to ourselves. It gave one a wonderfully smug feeling of superiority to drift slowly past the turrets of Chaumont or Amboise, alone and unseen—like walking along the corridors of the Louvre after closing-time; to watch them at first from a distance, transparent, white and unreal, slowly growing, vanishing round a bend, bursting into view again unexpectedly huge and forbidding; and to see them all the time from the river which they were built to dominate; which was their *raison d'être*.

When we arrived in Saumur, after a fortnight on the river, we stowed *Blue Arrow* in the car and took her to Brittany for an Atlantic after-taste. In the sheltered bay of Concarneau we paddled her round lighthouses and rocks; then, by the simple expedient of pushing two paddle-blades through the sleeves of a shirt, sailed with the tide up the estuary of the Belon, where the fat oysters wait all year round in their beds for customers to swallow them alive.

We did not meet another canoe either on the Dordogne or

on the Loire. Canoeing is a dying sport because the young have taken to Vespas, and the middle-aged associate it in their minds with the horrors of camping. Yet it is the ideal cure for people who, like myself, suffer from holiday neurosis —a common affliction not mentioned in psychiatric text-books; the people for whom lazing on a beach is hell, and pre-planned pleasure a guarantee of disappointment; quite apart from such minor symptoms as tourist's liver and sight-seer's eye.

After the first day on the Dordogne, every joint in my body cried out that it would never again submit to the ignominy of spending eight hours crouched like a Yogi in the bottom of a canoe; the next morning I was itching to get back into it. There is, no doubt, a grain of masochism in canoeing; but that, as every holiday neurotic readily understands, is just the beauty of it. You take your punishment first, then sit down to your *coq au vin*.

*Tu Felix Austria**

'I believed the worst about everybody, including myself, and
I was but seldom mistaken'—thus Johann Nestroy summed
up the Austrian *credo* a century ago; and he added the bitter
pun: 'The noblest nation is resignation.'

I had spent the happiest years of my youth in Vienna; but
on my last pre-war visit, in 1934, that *credo* seemed to have
come fearfully true. The capital of the truncated empire had
reached the depth of economic misery, cultural provincialism
and political brutality. The workers' model settlements—the
first Welfare State in miniature—had been shot to pieces by
the artillery of Dollfuss, the dwarf dictator; Austria was leading Europe in the art of civil war. A few months later, Dollfuss
himself was butchered in a Nazi *coup*, and a few years later the
Habsburg metropolis became the drab administrative centre
of an underprivileged province of Hitler's Reich. The seven
years' darkness had descended on the Danube.

When I revisited Vienna twenty years later, in 1954, I
found not a single person whom I had known before the war
—neither friend nor acquaintance, not a man, not a woman,
not a dog. I knew a number of Viennese in Paris, London,
New York and Tel Aviv; but in Vienna, nobody. They had

* First published in *The Observer*, 18.10.1959, under the title: 'Europe's
Serene Outpost'.

either emigrated or been killed in the gas chambers, the concentration camps, the war.

The majority of them had, of course, been Jews. I say 'of course', because the culture of pre-war Vienna had been an Austro-Judaic culture. It was the age of Freud and Adler, of Schnitzler, Hofmannsthal and Reinhardt, of Franz Kafka and Karl Kraus, of Peter Altenberg and Popper-Lynkeus, of Mahler and Schoenberg, of Werfel and Stefan Zweig. Out of a total population of two million, Vienna counted about a quarter-million Jews and, for better or worse, these acted like an iridescent film of oil spread over the surface of a sweet-water pool. The literary Establishment, the Press, the Bar, the cabarets were Austro-Judaic; in the Soccer League, the Jewish team, Hakoah, was usually among the top three—and soccer outdid even the Opera in arousing worshipful passion.

To appreciate post-war Austria, it is unavoidable to hark back to these facts, for, in the Freud–Schnitzler–Hofmannsthal age, the elimination of the Jewish element, and next to it of the Hungarian and Czech element, from Austrian culture seemed as unimaginable as, say, the elimination of the Welsh, Irish and Scottish ingredients from the culture of these islands.

That first post-war visit to the town in which nobody I had known was left came as a painful shock. The Prater, Europe's most glorious playground, was in ruins; the Opera a burnt-out shell; my boarding-school in the Soviet zone of occupation; the Grand Hotel a Russian barracks, where oxen were slaughtered in the ballroom. The houses, the shops, the veteran tram-cars, battered and shabby, were reduced to Asian standards; the people in the streets crumpled and bedraggled; the svelte damsels bloated and coarse-skinned from undernourishment. The Hungarian, Czech, Croat, Slovene accents, those essential discords and counterpoints of the Austrian symphony, no longer echoed through the lobbies of the University, in the theatres and cafés with the cracked marble panelling.

After the disintegration, in 1918, of the Austro-Hungarian

monarchy, Vienna, though impoverished and diminished in stature, had nevertheless remained the cultural centre of its vanished empire. But in 1945, almost overnight, the town found itself bodily displaced from the centre of Europe to its eastern periphery. It became once more what it had been under the Turkish sieges: the foremost outpost of Western Christendom.

It is this extreme change of destiny which makes the example of post-war Austria so significant for Europe. For, if the politically and morally bankrupt Austria of the 1930s was leading in the European race towards self-destruction, the Austria of the 1950s may be regarded as a symbol of Europe's phenomenal powers of moral regeneration.

Thus by an astonishing twist of history, the two great Austrian political parties—Socialists and Catholics, commonly called Reds and Blacks—who started in 1934 the series of European civil wars, today form the stablest coalition-regime in Europe. It began under the Russian occupation in 1945, as a kind of war-time emergency marriage; it has now lasted, uninterruptedly, for fifteen solid years, and if all goes well may yet lead to a silver wedding—a thing unprecedented in the annals of parliamentary democracy. *Tu felix Austria nubes* seems to have assumed a new meaning: the Habsburgs acquired their territories by marrying judiciously; the politicians of post-war Austria secured stability and prosperity by adopting, metaphorically, the same method.

In spite of their diametrically opposed philosophies there is in the realm of practical action very little indeed to distinguish Red from Black. In foreign politics their attitude is identical: an unambiguously Western orientation within the framework of formal neutrality, imposed by the treaty of 1955. In internal politics, each party recognises the other's zone of influence: Vienna is traditionally Red, the countryside traditionally Black; as for the economy, Butskellism reigns unchallenged and has within the last ten years transformed an extremely impoverished, starving country into one with a hard and sound economy, based on low prices, low wages, low rents, and priding itself on one of the hardest currencies in Europe. So successful was the coalition experiment that during the electoral campaign last spring both parties were asking for votes, not, Heaven forbid, to outdo the other side, but to preserve the balance at a fifty-fifty level.

The coalition marriage is, of course, not a perfect idyll. It makes Parliament sometimes resemble a stagnant pool, where the clash of ideas is replaced by bickering and intrigue. In all branches of Government, Civil Service and administration, posts are allocated according to a fixed ratio between the parties, which sometimes interferes with the choice of the ablest candidate. It is a standard Austrian joke that if at a public convenience the attendant at the 'Ladies' is a Black, the attendant at the 'Gents' must be a Red; and this is not far from being literally true. Yet, bearing in mind the history of the first Austrian Republic and the post-war history of some other European countries, these blemishes are relatively small.

It would be a mistake, however, to explain the spectacular recovery of Austria by the coalition experiment alone, unique though it may be. Rather, the stability and duration of the coalition should be regarded as a consequence of a psychological change whose roots go much deeper than parliamentary politics. It is a change born out of an intensity of suffering which no other Western nation has known. For the eastern part of Austria, including Vienna, is the only country of the free West which was under Russian military occupation—which was caught on the other side of the Iron Curtain at the height of war-time savagery—and then released to make a new start.

On Easter Sunday, March 31, 1945, the Red Army broke through the Austrian frontier and, a few days later, Vienna was cut off from the world: without electricity, food supplies, water, sanitation, newspapers or radio communications. The history of that dark interregnum until the arrival of the Western Allies in Vienna has not yet been written, and the Viennese talk only reluctantly about it.

One of the reasons for this lies in the still unpublished figures of a certain Austrian office whose lists contain 86,000 recorded cases of rape, reported by the victims to obtain prophylactic treatment against venereal disease; the ages range from eleven to eighty. For several months the hospitals in Vienna performed abortions as an emergency measure, legalised by the provisional Government. Since the majority of the victims must have been reluctant to report, their total number is estimated at about 30 per cent of all female adults who had not fled; in the countryside, the proportion was much higher. Those who had not fled belonged mostly to the working classes and poorer strata of the population, who may have been inclined to greet the Russians as their liberators from Nazi oppression.

One is reluctant to stir up the memory of war-time horrors, and it must be admitted that what the West did to Hiroshima was more frightful than what the Russians did to Vienna. But one cannot talk of post-war Japan without mentioning the Bomb, nor of post-war Austria without mentioning the traumatic experience which it suffered. It ended once and for all Communist sympathies, both among the people and in the intelligentsia (Austria has no Nennis, Sartres, Picassos or Deans of Canterbury); but it had psychological consequences which went deeper than that. For, however painful the experiences of France, the Low Countries, Denmark and Norway under Nazi occupation had been, the shock that Vienna suffered was of a more extreme, a quasi-archaic nature, and penetrated into deeper strata in the nation's psyche. It became the turning-point in Austrian history.

Up to 1918 the Austrians regarded themselves as the head of the multi-national monarchy. After 1918 they became a guillotined head, pining for its lost body; after 1945 they discovered, for the first time, that they were a nation in their own right, economically viable and culturally self-contained.

When the Turkish siege was lifted at the turn of the seventeenth century, Vienna burst into bloom—into the golden age of Austrian Baroque. The end of the occupation regime in 1955 brought a repetition of the phenomenon on a minor scale—a revival of optimism and *joie de vivre*. It was epitomised in the gaudy, maudlin, deeply moving ballyhoo at the re-opening of the holy of holies, the rebuilt Opera House. A year later, the Hungarian tragedy on their doorstep reminded them that, though Austria was freed, the European siege was not yet lifted and that Vienna was still—or again—a frontier town. They rose to the occasion in a remarkable manner: thousands of Hungarian refugees owe their lives to the Austrian rescue teams, composed of volunteers, who operated along the frontier at considerable risk, and to the sang-froid of the Austrian Government.

On the whole, Nestroy, the idol of the Viennese, who always expected the worst of them, seems to have been proved wrong. If the Austrians have sinned—mainly, perhaps, by passive complicity—they have done hard penance. They have also shed their self-pitying nostalgia for the glories of the past, and embarked on a new experiment: to make a nation which is not Austro-Hungarian, nor Austro-German, nor Austro-anything, but Austrian.

For the time being it is no more than an experiment, and the outcome difficult to foresee. It may grow into something staunch, worthy and provincial; or succumb to the temptations of the tourist trade and lose its identity. But my guess is that in the end the spirit of Vienna will prevail: for—to quote Hans Weigel—there is, after all, no other town in the world where the dentists play the 'cello so beautifully.

The Ubiquitous Presence*

My last visit to Hungary dates back to 1935. My memories of it have faded like old photographs and at the same time acquired the maudlin colouring which nostalgia lends to the past. But I found a record of that visit in a passage I wrote some years later in an autobiographical book.

Within a few days I had met nearly every Hungarian writer and his retinue; for the more prominent were always followed to their cafés by a suite of wives, ex-wives, mistresses, and the wives' and mistresses' boy friends. The latter were a tribe of extremely correct, nice and well-behaved young men who felt deeply honoured by being admitted to the society of celebrated writers.

It was a strange society, and quite different in atmosphere from literary cliques in Paris, London or Berlin. Post-war Hungary was a dwarf-state, with a population of seven million, of whom the majority were semi-literate peasants. Like Austria, it lived in a chronic economic depression, punctuated by acute crises. But unlike Austria and other small nations, it had no ties, through a shared language, with the cultures of larger neighbours; the Magyars are an isolated ethnic enclave in Europe, and their only relatives are the distant Finns. Hungarian writers could only secure a larger audience by emigrating, and learning to write in the language of their adopted country. But to abandon his native language and traditions means in most cases death to the writer, and his transformation into a nondescript, cosmopolitan journalist or literary hack. Hungary's

* First published in *Ten Years After—A Commemoration of the Tenth Anniversary of the Hungarian Revolution*, ed. Tamas Aczel (London, 1966).

main export since the First World War had been reporters, script-writers, film producers, magazine editors, commercial artists, actresses, and manufacturers of topical best-sellers—the international demi-monde of the arts and letters. They were strewn all over the world by that centrifugal force which is generated when an exceptional amount of talent is cooped up without means of expression in a small country.*

This, I now realise, though partly true, was nevertheless grossly unfair. No doubt, that demi-monde exists and keeps spawning in the cafés and goulash bistros from Vienna to New York and Tokio; but this is only the conspicuous, sleazy part of the Hungarian export. Its less conspicuous, in-comparably more valuable elements were absorbed in the physics, mathematics and biology departments of univer-sities; in orchestras and string quartets, in hospitals, research laboratories and government agencies. I have before me a list of 300 names, ranging from art historians to zoologists, and from the prominent to the world famous. I do not think there has been a migration of scholars and artists on a similar scale since the fall of Byzantium.

Part of the explanation of the phenomenon is, as I have just said, the ethnic isolation, the pronounced minority mentality of the Hungarian enclave in its Germanic and Slavonic surroundings. But there is an additional factor to be considered: a large proportion of the list before me con-sists of Hungarian Jews. This is only to be expected in view of the fact that one third of the pre-war population of Budapest was Jewish, and provided the bulk of the intelli-gentsia in that predominantly rural, semi-feudal country. *Qua* Jews, they were conscious of their precarious minority status in a small country intensely conscious of its minority status. They were a minority within a minority—a minority of the second order, so to speak. If Toynbee's theory of 'challenge and response' has any truth in it—as I believe it has—then the pressure of such an intense challenge could not fail to provoke an explosive response.

* *The Invisible Writing* (Collins with Hamish Hamilton, London, 1954).

I shall not attempt to explain how the Jews in Hungary (and Austria) came to occupy this numerically disproportionate position in the intellectual and professional life of their countries: the explanation can be found in any serious book on their social history. But the causes were social, not racial. The Jews of Central and Eastern Europe are an extremely mixed race; a substantial proportion of them is supposed to be not of semitic, but of Caucasian (Khasar) origin; and the Jews of Hungary, Poland, Russia are not only in appearance but also in the relative distribution of blood groups, more closely related to their respective host nations than to each other. A gene transmitted from ancient Canaan must by now have become a rarity.

If one compares the Hungarian emigration with others— such as the Russian emigration after the Revolution of 1917, or the German anti-Nazi emigration of 1933–39, one finds an important difference in motivation and structure. The 'white' Russians and the anti-Nazis (again mostly Jews) emigrated under duress during a relatively short critical period. They were pushed out of their countries by a repellant force. The Hungarian talent export on the other hand has been going on steadily for about two generations, and (except for the short burst after the defeat of the 1956 revolution) embraced a politically heterogeneous group of all persuasions, who emigrated on their own initiative, without immediate duress—not so much repelled, as attracted by the larger possibilities of intellectual or material fulfilment offered by the world outside. The Russian or German emigration was a flight for survival; the Hungarian was more of a brain-drain —as this country is experiencing it now—on a proportionately larger and intenser scale.

We can only conclude—as George Mikes would put it— that if there are intelligent beings on Mars, they almost certainly will greet each other with *kezét csókolom*; and that the mysterious red spot on the planet, discovered by Russian astronomers, must be a large paprika mine.

Books in Review

Of Dogs and Men

1

Battle for the Mind; a Physiology of Conversion and Brainwashing. By William Sargant.*

'Pavlov's experiments on dogs are so remarkably applicable to certain problems of human behaviour that the remark "men are not dogs" becomes at times almost irrelevant.' We have been conditioned to a meek acceptance of statements of this kind, particularly if the authority is a psychiatrist at a famous London teaching hospital. We may wonder, though, in just what kind of situation our behaviour becomes the most dog-like. The author's answer is: in the process of being converted to a religious or political creed; when suffering from acute war neurosis; and when being psychoanalysed.

Dr. Sargant's theory was developed in two stages. The first is related to Pavlov, the second to Wesley. In 1944, at the time of the Normandy invasion, he was treating acute battle neuroses by abreaction therapy under drugs: the patient was made to relive his terrifying experiences, or imaginary terrors suggested to him, such as being trapped in a burning tank:

* Reviewed in *The Observer*, October 1959.

> Outbursts of fear and anger thus deliberately induced and stimulated to a crescendo by the therapist would frequently be followed by a sudden emotional collapse. . . .

If all went well, the patient's symptoms were relieved or disappeared altogether after one or several of these artificially induced collapses. At this stage, Dr. Sargant and a colleague 'remembered how, in some of Pavlov's dogs, the Leningrad flood had accidentally abolished the recently conditioned behaviour patterns implanted by him. Was the same thing happening in some of our patients who had suddenly collapsed in this way?' They answered the question in the affirmative, and this affirmation is a cornerstone of Dr. Sargant's theory.

Pavlov's work had shown that a dog will suffer a nervous breakdown under conditions of conflict and stress. This is induced by over-excitation; by creating tension and anxiety; by confusing signals; and by lowering the dog's physical resistance. When the stress exceeds the critical, or 'transmarginal', limit of what a dog can stand, 'protective brain inhibition' sets in, which passes through several phases, from dullness and apathy to the 'ultra-paradoxical' phase where some of the habitual responses are reversed. The dog may also sink into a quasi-hypnotic state, or display symptoms resembling hysteria. Apart from these artificially induced disorders, Pavlov had also occasion to observe the consequences of an unexpected natural shock: in the 1924 flood the cages were inundated and the terrified dogs saved from drowning only in the nick of time. Afterwards, some dogs lost 'their recently implanted behaviour patterns', and were frightened at the sight of water seeping in under the door.

Dr. Sargant discovered in 1944 that similar symptoms were displayed by his war-shocked patients: parallels between their behaviour and Pavlov's dogs 'leapt to the eye'. It was all a matter of 'protective brain inhibition'; the complexities of mental disorder became beautifully simplified:

> Descriptions of hysteria in all psychiatric textbooks record

bizarre symptoms which do not become always understandable, except with Pavlov's mechanistic experiments on dogs.

The terror of the drugged patient, before he collapsed in
emotional exhaustion, erased his recently acquired symptoms, as the drowning experience had erased the reflexes
implanted in the dogs. The psychoanalytical couch lost its
aura of mystery:

> Just as Pavlov's dogs remained sensitive to the original cause
> of their mental disruption—namely, water seeping in under-
> neath the laboratory door during the Leningrad flood—so
> patients tend to become highly sensitised to the therapist who
> causes them repeated emotional upheavals.

This explained the patient's dependence on the analyst,
the convert's devotion to the preacher, the prisoner's suggestibility by the brain-washer. John Wesley's fire-and-brim-
stone preaching had the same physiological effect on the
prospective convert's brain as the flood on the dogs and the
shock on the patient.

> It now seemed possible, in fact, that many of the results
> which were being achieved by abreaction under drugs were
> essentially the same as those obtained, not only by Wesley and
> other religious leaders, but by modern 'brain-washers'. . . .

To prove his thesis, Dr. Sargant takes us on a conducted
tour of Voodoo worshippers and Chinese Communists, snake-
handlers and witch-hunters, ancient and modern. There
is also a short halt on the road to Damascus; here is the
voice of our Pavlovian guide explaining what exactly happened on that spot:

> 'And the Lord said, I am Jesus whom thou persecutest: it is
> hard for thee to kick against the pricks. And he trembling and
> astonished said, Lord, what wilt thou have me to do?'
> A state of transmarginal inhibition seems to have followed his
> acute state of nervous excitement. Total collapse, hallucinations
> and an increased state of suggestibility appear to have super-
> vened. Other inhibitory hysterical manifestations are also
> reported:

'And Saul arose from the earth; and when his eyes were opened he saw no man. . . .'

After a delightful chapter on 'brain-washing in ancient times', contributed by Robert Graves, we turn to the 'eliciting of confessions' in modern times, in which we are shown Evans and Christie in London, Stypulsky and Weissberg in Moscow, confessing in various states of transmarginal inhibition. The grains of truth in all this are grains of truisms; the analogies are stretched and inflated like bubblegums; the total effect is one of acute embarrassment—the more embarrassing as the author repeatedly quotes me, with apparent approval, as a witness.

In his introductory and closing remarks, Dr. Sargant points out that he deliberately confined himself to the discussion of 'mechanistic and physiological methods' of influencing the human brain, 'rather than scouring the metaphysical ocean for hidden mysteries'. But his book—and indeed the whole history of psychology—proves that the mechanistic approach (whether inspired by arrogance or modesty) is sterile; that it does not lead to a part-truth but to a travesty of the whole truth. No healer of the mind can work without a conscious or implied system of values, without wetting his skin in the 'metaphysical ocean'. Dr. Sargant's metaphysical bias, the bias of a Pavlovite convert, is evident on nearly every page. To say, for instance, that the drug-cum-terror treatment of battle casualties 'was less helpful in the treatment of chronic neurotics' is surely a whale of an understatement; one might as well say 'application of the stomach pump was less helpful in the treatment of kidney stones'.

Or this:

So close were the similarities between these [war neuroses] and canine neuroses that it seemed more improbable than ever that many current psychological theories about the origin of human neuroses and other abnormalities of behaviour were correct; unless it be conceded that Pavlov's dogs had sub-conscious minds and also super-egos, egos and ids.

This amounts to the syllogism: dogs have no subconscious mind; dog-neuroses resemble certain human neuroses; therefore humans have no subconscious mind, and Freud, Adler, Kretschmer, Jung, etc., are wrong.

Pavlov created an artificially closed world into which only the emotions of hunger, rage and fear were admitted; in which dogs strapped and harnessed on the laboratory table were reduced to reflex robots. The conclusions drawn from the number of drops which these sub-canine artifacts discharge through rubber tubes from salivary glands which have been transplanted to the surface of their cheeks are, I suggest, totally irrelevant to the motives of Saul's conversion into Paul —irrelevant not only to the theologian, but also to psychological science.

2

The Unquiet Mind—The Autobiography of a Physician In Psychological Medicine. By William Sargant*

Psychiatry is experiencing its *Götterdämmerung*. The twilight of doubt has descended on the therapeutic couch; the aura of the omniscient, benevolent magician is paling. From a god-like figure he is being transformed into a competent technician prescribing tranquilisers, anti-depressants, electroshocks, leucotomies, as, in the days before Charcot and Freud, his less sophisticated forebears prescribed purges, bleedings, cold baths, or whippings. The pendulum is in full swing back from the mentalistic to the physicalistic approach. One of the most eminent and radical representatives of this trend is

* Reviewed in *The Observer*, 25.6.1967. Dr. Sargant's autobiography was published eight years after his *Battle for the Mind*. The theory he had developed in that earlier book occupies a central position in the autobiography, and as readers could not be expected to remember it, I had to refer to it once more.

Dr. William Sargant, Head of the Psychiatry Department at St. Thomas's Hospital and a former President of the Section of Psychiatry of the Royal Society of Medicine.

One of the causes of the swing was growing disenchantment with psychoanalytic forms of treatment—their unpredictable duration and uncertain prospects. The teachings of Freud and Jung have permeated literature, art, anthropology and philosophy; as a practical therapy for the masses they have failed. The word 'masses' is justified. One half of all hospital beds in England and America is occupied by psychiatric cases. Worse than that: nearly a third of all patients who consult a physician turn out to be in need of psychological treatment. To analyse each case by Freudian or Jungian methods over a number of years is a practical impossibility. Psychoanalysis, to paraphrase Veblen, is the therapy of the leisure classes.

Another, positive cause of the swing of the pendulum was the striking progress of psychopharmacology and—more indirectly—of neurosurgery. Discounting the sensational claims for psychiatric wonder-drugs which are periodically launched in the Press, the fact remains that some of the previously intractable psychoses have begun to yield to chemotherapy; certain types of mental deficiency in children can now be traced to the lack of a specific enzyme; and there are indications that a biochemical basis for schizophrenia —or at least some forms of it—will be discovered in the foreseeable future.

Up to a point, then, one can agree with Dr. Sargant's advocacy of a 'physicalistic' approach to mental illness. But unfortunately he displays pronounced symptoms of 'bathwaterism'. This useful term was coined by the biologist R. F. Ewer; and throughout Dr. Sargant's autobiography one is aware of the gurgling of the bath-water as it carries the baby down the drain. He has no use for the concept of the unconscious mind, for 'Freudian and other metaphysical beliefs' (p. 218); or for the concept of mind itself—for he insists (my italics) 'that the mind (*conceived merely as the brain*) would in the end be treated as practically as the liver, the lungs and all similar organs' (p. 121); and that 'brain function [i.e. mental disorder] can best be brought to normal in exactly the same way that bodily functions have most easily been brought back to normal' (p. 228). This last quotation is from a lecture Dr. Sargant gave to the Royal College of Physicians with the title 'Psychiatric Treatment in General Teaching Hospitals: a Plea for a Mechanistic Approach'; and he chose, as a motto for his lecture, a remark from an after-dinner talk by that paragon of medical discretion, Lord Moran: 'The physician who knows what is wrong with the patient and has an effective remedy in his hands can cut the cackle. He has no need of it.'

The choice of title and motto makes one pause. For, whatever the 'effective remedy' (tablets, injections, surgery, shock therapy or what-have-you), the soothing cackle designed to reassure the patient and make him trust the healer is an essential part of the cure; and particularly, of course, if it is a psychiatric cure. So much so, that placebos—dummy pills—have been shown to act often as 'effective remedies'; and that new drugs are now frequently tested by the double-blind method, where even the nurses are not allowed to know which patient is given the drug and which the placebo.

The massive experimental evidence for the influence of such 'mentalistic' and mostly unconscious factors on the effectiveness of physical remedies is passed in silence in Dr. Sargant's book. There are other omissions. 'The main purpose of this autobiography,' the Foreword says, 'is to describe the fascinating progress that has taken place during the last thirty years in the discovery of medical and surgical approaches to the treatment of the mind of man.' Yet the fundamental concept of psychosomatic disorder is not mentioned a single time in the book—although in one passage the author cheerfully states that a soldier may suffer from 'motivated, piles': motivated, that is, by his wish to obtain his discharge from the army. Nor is there any mention—although this has a direct bearing on the physicalistic approach to mental illness—of the LSD type of hallucinogenic drugs, which provide the psychiatrist with the means to induce the symptoms of psychotic states—and thus with a clue to the possible biochemial causation underlying them.

None of the various neurphysiological theories of emotion (from James–Lange through Cannon–Bard, to Lashley, Magoun and Papez–MacLean) is mentioned by Dr. Sargant. There is only one chapter devoted to theoretical considerations of a general nature (Chapter 12), and this is based on Pavlov's experiments on dogs in the first decades of this century, which form the cornerstone of Dr. Sargant's credo. He relates how he became acquainted with Pavlov's experiments in 1944. At that time he was engaged in treating soldiers sent back from Normandy with acute battle neurosis, by means of abreaction therapy:

> . . . We invented fearful and dangerous situations and suggested them to the patient under drugs. . . . For example, we might excitedly tell a member of the Royal Tank Corps who had broken down in battle that he was trapped in his burning tank . . . If we could raise the crescendo of a patient's outburst to a grand finale of rage or terror, a state of temporary emotional collapse might follow. A patient might well be helped . . . So we developed a successful technique of deliberately inducing collapse by stimulating emotions of anger or fear in our semi-drugged patients: which was helped by our studying Pavlov's experiments.

At this stage Dr. Sargant thought he had discovered a parallel between the behaviour of Pavlov's dogs and the behaviour of his patients. This analogy was then extended to explain the prisoner's suggestibility to brain-washing, Evans confessing to the murder which Christie committed, and Saul's conversion on the road to Damascus: 'here was material for an over-all physiological thesis' (p. 119).

It is not a sign of the layman's squeamishness to feel repelled by the cruelty of this abreaction-through-terror method (which worked only on a limited range of cases and was subsequently abandoned); a number of Dr. Sargant's colleagues were equally scandalised by it at the time. Yet the tenuous Pavlovian analogy had meanwhile blossomed into an 'over-all thesis', expounded in Dr. Sargant's *Battle of the Mind*. He tells us twice over (pp. 119 and 175) that it has sold 'over 200,000 copies in various languages'.

One of the leading neurophysiologists of our time, D. O. Hebb of McGill, wrote nearly twenty years ago: 'Pavlov has deservedly had a great influence on psychology, and his theory has not been rejected because it is too physiological, but because it does not agree with experiment.' The exclusive Pavlovian bias of Dr. Sargant's book, and his refusal to pay attention to alternative schools of thought, invalidates its claim to be a report on the progress of psychiatry 'in the last thirty years'. To judge it by its literary merits would be unfair, as the author has no literary pretensions. One is nevertheless left slightly gasping by his comment on the 'group of English intellectuals who [in 1939] had fled to America with the expressed intention of not returning until the war was over. I met some of these and pitied them for their lost sense of honour and their shabby excuses for leaving what seemed a sinking ship.'

If this is what a psychiatrist in an eminent position has to offer us as an explanation of the motives of Wystan Auden or Aldous Huxley, then the profession is truly in a state of *Götterdämmerung*.

Of Geese and Men

On Aggression *by Konrad Lorenz, with a Foreword by Sir Julian Huxley.**

Konrad Lorenz is mainly known in this country as the author of two delightful books on animal lore (*King Solomon's Ring* and *Man Meets Dog*); but he is also, as Sir Julian Huxley says in his Foreword, 'the father of modern ethology'. This new science is usually defined as the comparative study of the behaviour of animals in their natural environment; but this description applies to the amateur bird-watcher as well, and conveys no idea of the ethologist's sophisticated techniques, which make the classical naturalist look hopelessly old-fashioned.

The rise of ethology in the after-war years had the exhilarating effect of a March breeze rattling against the tightly shut laboratory windows of American Behaviourism, where generations of graduate students had been taught that the principal task of animal psychologists was to count the number of times a white albino rat confined in a Skinner box will press a lever to obtain a food pellet. The orthodox Behaviourist of the mid-century regarded organisms as essentially passive masses of software which could only be

* Reviewed in *The Observer*, 18.9.1966.

studied profitably in the artificial environment of the laboratory; no wonder they did not like this new European heresy. Not until 1962 did the august *Annual Review of Psychology* print for the first time an article on ethology; but in the meantime, Lorenz's research station at Seewiesen in Bavaria, a kind of naturalist's Disneyland, has become a place of pilgrimage for students from all over the world.

Thus we have every reason to be grateful to Lorenz, even if we cannot always follow him on this latest, semi-philosophical excursion which, in the German original, has the ambitious title *Über das sogenannte Böse*.

It is not easy to give a brief summary of its contents. To start with, Lorenz states that the action of the predator killing its prey, which belongs to a different species, is not 'genuine' aggression because 'the lion in the dramatic moment before he springs is in no way angry'. Real aggression is mainly intra-specific—directed against members of the aggressor's own species. It has its positive functions: the jealous defence of the territory occupied by a couple of swans ensures the evenly balanced distribution of the members of a group in a given area, and the mating fights between rivals favour the sexual selection of the strongest and most gallant specimens.

This much is classical Darwinism. Now Lorenz turns to the problem of the genetic origin of the binding forces which hold families and groups together. The simplest social organisation is the herd, flock or school of animals which travel in close formation in the same direction, 'drawn together as by a magnet'. They are 'animals totally devoid of aggression;' but their association is, Lorenz says, impersonal and anonymous *precisely because they lack aggression*. 'A personal bond, an individual friendship is found only in animals with highly developed intra-specific aggression.' Moreover, the personal bond of affection between individuals (with or without a sexual factor) is not only always *combined* with aggression, but is phylogenetically *derived* from aggression. To prove this hypothesis, Lorenz relies heavily on his observations of the so-called triumph ceremony of the greylag goose which, he says, prompted him to write the present book.

The ceremony evolved in several stages. Intra-specific aggression has its useful functions; yet it must not degenerate into lethal fighting; so evolution compromised by preserving the animal's aggressive drive, but provided it with inhibitory mechanisms against killing its like. One such mechanism is the *ritualisation* (Huxley) of fighting into a more or less symbolic duel which is instantly terminated by a specific gesture of submission by one of the combatants; another is *redirection* (Tinbergen) of the attack from its original object to a substitute. Ritualisation and redirection combined gave rise to the triumph ceremony: the goose watches while the gander performs a symbolic attack against an imaginary foe and, after scoring a symbolic victory, returns to her with a triumphant cackle.

In the course of evolution, however, this ritual has acquired a new purpose: from a behaviour pattern motivated by aggression it has changed 'into a love ceremony which forms a strong tie between those who participate in it. This means neither more nor less than converting the mutually repelling effect of aggression into its opposite. Thus it forms a *bond* between individuals. The bond that holds a goose-pair together for life is the triumph ceremony and not the sexual relations between mates.'

Here we have an example of the highly original results of painstaking ethological observation. But unfortunately Lorenz also regards the behaviour of the goose as a paradigm for the bonds which unite human communities; it is surprising how strong the temptation can be, in otherwise ultra-cautious scientists, to take flight on the treacherous wings of analogy, at the risk of sharing the fate of Icarus.

The main criticism directed at the ethologists has always been that their favourite objects of study were birds and fishes with extremely stereotyped rituals which are not necessarily characteristic of animal behaviour in general. Recent research on the behaviour of primate societies has shown that ritualised actions and signals certainly play a part in preventing conflict and maintaining hierarchic order, but provide no support for Lorenz's thesis that the bonds of affection among members of the group originated in sub-limated aggression rites, as in the goose. Thus the famous studies of the Harlows on the social life of rhesus monkeys led them to postulate several types of affectional bonds which 'can only be understood by conceiving love as a number of love- or affectional-systems, and not as a single emotion'. There is no evidence of any of these bonds being derived from ritualised aggression.

Lorenz believes that the evil in man originates in an evolutionary shortcoming: because he lacks the deadly natural weapons of other carnivores, he also lacks the built-in inhibitory mechanisms 'preventing the killing of con-specifics until, all of a sudden, the invention of artificial weapons upset the equilibrium of killing potential and social inhibitions'. Selective pressure did the rest to produce a species of intra-specific killers.

This is an arguable hypothesis, even if it can reflect only part of the truth; but there is no need to go into it because, as Lorenz himself points out, the holocausts of human history were not caused by murders committed for personal motives by aggressive individuals, but by 'militant enthusiasm' *ad majorem gloriam* in the service of a cause. This is the point at which a serious discussion of man's predicament could start; but unfortunately we are once more referred to the goose. Lorenz sees the phylogenetic origin of 'man's overpowering urge to espouse a cause' in a phenomenon he discovered thirty years ago: the 'imprinting' of newly hatched birds, which attach themselves to the first moving object, and re-main forever emotionally fixated on it. Each species of animal has a critical period of 'maximum imprintability'—in ducklings, for instance, it is 13 to 16 hours after hatching. In human beings, Lorenz says, imprinting with a cause 'can take its full effect only once in an individual's life; this critical period is during and shortly after puberty'. One cannot help being reminded of Whitehead's warning against 'misplaced concreteness'. Besides, at least one outstanding younger ethologist, E. H. Hess, is of a different opinion: 'In the human being one could thus theoretically place the end of maximum inprintability at about five and a half months of age.'

Behaviourism started by rejecting the pathetic fallacy; it ended up by replacing the anthropomorphic view of the rat with a ratomorphic view of man. Now Professor Lorenz seems to offer us an anseromorphic view (*anser* = goose). But it would be churlish to grudge the Sage of Seewiesen this lusty gallop on a hobby horse—the more so as the remedies he has to offer mankind are all wholly laudable; sport to canalise aggression, art and science to sublimate it, the promotion of international friendship, and humour as an antidote to militant enthusiasm. On this programme we would all agree; and if you land on the side of the angels, it does not much matter how you got there.

Of Apes and Men

The Naked Ape—A Zoologist's Study of the Human Animal.
By Desmond Morris.*

> There are one hundred and ninety-three living species of monkeys and apes. One hundred and ninety-two of them are covered with hair. The exception is a naked ape, self-named *Homo sapiens* . . . I am a zoologist and the naked ape is an animal. He is therefore fair game for my pen . . .

These provocative sentences are from the opening of Dr. Morris' 'zoological portrait' of man. It is based on three sources: the fossil record concerning our ancestry; the ethologist's studies of primate behaviour; and the observation of social science concerning 'the major contemporary cultures of the naked ape itself'. This is a more ambitious enterprise than some earlier attempts at a diagnosis of man's condition based on the behaviour of animals—Pavlov's dogs, the Behaviourist's rats, or Lorenz's greylag geese. These have yielded analogies which were at best of limited value, but often misleading and fraught with disastrous philosophical conclusions. More recently there has been a spate of extremely valuable field-studies on the behaviour of primate societies, which are evidently more relevant to us than rats or geese. Dr. Morris utilises this new mass of data with much

* Reviewed in *The Observer*, 15.10.1967.

ingenuity to shed new light on our own odd ways of 'feeding, sleeping, fighting, mating and rearing the young'.

He regards as the decisive episode in man's evolution the change-over from a tree-dwelling, fruit-munching, lackadaisical creature to a carnivorous predator of the open plains, hunting in packs. Man's dual personality, and every uniquely human characteristic, is said to originate in this event: upright posture, growth of the brain, weapons, tools, family bonds, tribal cohesion, the evolution of language. This chapter on 'Origins' is perhaps the most stimulating in the book.

The next is concerned with Sex, and here the zoological portrait, enriched by Freudian hues, has some remarkable surprises to offer to the layman and not-so-layman. Our fleshy earlobes, we are told, absent in all other primates and described by anatomists as 'useless, fatty excrescences', are in fact erogenous zones which, in sexual excitement, become engorged with blood, swollen and hypersensitive; moreover, 'there are cases on record of both males and females actually reaching orgasm as a result of earlobe-stimulation'. We also have to revise our ideas about the functions of the female breast. It is 'predominantly a sexual signalling device rather than an expanded milk-machine'. The females of other primate species are flat-chested compared to ours, with pendulous breasts and longer nipples, which make them into more efficient milk-machines. The protruding, hemispherical breast of the naked ape, on the other hand, makes life more difficult, because it tends to block the baby's nostrils while it is suckling and cause it to struggle for air—often interpreted by anxious mothers as a refusal to feed. Another fascinating bit of information is that 80 per cent of all mothers (at least in the U.S.A. where these studies were made) cradle their babies in their left arm against the left side of their bodies—and that this applies to right-handed and left-handed women alike. The explanation offered is that the embryo becomes 'imprinted' in the womb by the sound of the mother's heartbeat, which then acquires a calming effect on the infant.

Particularly rewarding are the minute descriptions of the changes in facial expression and bodily posture as unconscious threat or appeasement signals in man and ape:

> We cannot intimidate our opponents by erecting our body hair. We still do it in moments of great shock, but as a signal it is of little use. In other respects we can do much better. Our very nakedness, which prevents us from bristling effectively, gives us the chance to send powerful flushing and paling signals. We can go 'white with rage', 'red with anger', or 'pale with fear'. It is the white colour we have to watch for here: this spells activity. If it is combined with other actions that signal attack, then it is a vital danger signal. If it is combined with other actions that signal fear, then it is a panic signal. It is caused by the activation of the sympathetic nervous system, the 'go' system, and it is not to be treated lightly. The reddening, on the other hand, is less worrying: it is caused by the frantic counter-balancing attempts of the parasympathetic system, and indicates that the 'go' system is already being undermined. The angry, red-faced opponent who faces you is far less likely to attack than the white-faced, tight-lipped one.

Here the ethologist's training in the observation and analysis of animal behaviour is used to best effect, and is indeed capable of shedding new light on the evolutionary origins of some of our strange antics and social rites. That it is not a very flattering light should not be held against him.

In a word, the 'zoological portrait' reveals a number of features in our complexion—amusing, disgusting or just odd —which otherwise would pass unnoticed; and when you look into the mirror after reading the book, you won't look quite the same. The question is whether this revised image is closer to the essence of the human condition—or whether it is a different type of caricature, drawn by exaggerating precisely those simian features which the naive idealist's portrait ignores, and ignoring those which he legitimately values as specifically and exclusively human.

The trouble with the zoological portrait is not that it offends, but that it over-simplifies and thereby distorts. To be fair, the author is partly aware of this. 'Because of the size of the task,' he writes in his introduction, 'it will be necessary to over-simplify in some manner. The way I shall do this is largely to ignore the detailed ramifications of technology and verbalisation, and concentrate instead on those aspects of our lives that have obvious counterparts in other species.' But to leave out of account 'technology and verbalisation'— that is to say, language, science and art, the essential trademarks of our species—leads inevitably not only to a *simplified* but to a *distorted* picture, because these activities permeate and transform even those aspects of behaviour which we share with other species, such as 'feeding, fighting, mating and care of the young'.

Take the most crucial of these: fighting. Dr. Morris recognises only three causes of human aggressiveness: asserting one's place in the social hierarchy; defence of the family territory; defence of the territory of the group (pp. 148, 182). It follows that all human wars are waged for 'territorial defence' or 'territorial expansion' (p. 176)— which, historically, is simply untrue. Religious wars, dynastic wars, ideological wars, play a dominant part in human history, but have no place in the zoologist's account, because religions, dynasties and ideologies all hinge on the 'ramifications of verbalisation' which he decided to ignore. Language is a specifically human blessing and curse, which facilitates understanding *within* social groups, but accentuates the differences in traditions and beliefs *between* groups. By regarding the defence of territory as the only source of conflict, the zoological approach fails to recognise the essential predicament of man—his urge to kill or get killed for a flag, a credo, a slogan, *ad majorem gloriam*.

To what extremes the zoological approach may lead is illustrated by the following passage:

> The insides of houses or flats can be decorated and filled with ornaments, bric-à-brac and personal belongings in profusion. This is usually explained as being done to make the place 'look nice'. In fact, it is the exact equivalent to another

territorial species depositing its personal scent on a landmark near its den. When you put a name on a door, or hang a painting on a wall, you are, in dog or wolf terms, for example, simply cocking your leg on them and leaving your personal mark there. Obsessive 'collecting' of specialised categories of objects occurs in certain individuals who, for some reason, experience an abnormally strong need to define their home territories in this way (pp. 183–84).

Perhaps Sotheby's will adopt the simplified method of conducting an auction indicated in this passage.

In his introduction, Dr. Morris assures us that it is not his intention 'to degrade our species by discussing it in crude animal terms'. Nobody acquainted with Dr. Morris' previous books can doubt the sincerity of this statement; but one may wonder whether it is not self-contradictory. In spite of this basic flaw, *The Naked Ape* does achieve its proclaimed purpose to make us 'take a long, hard look at ourselves as biological specimens and gain some understanding of our limitations'. It has never a dull page, and can be strongly recommended to readers able to savour its wealth of information without swallowing all of its conclusions.

Mysterium Tremendum[*]

1 The Living Stream

The theory of evolution has become a strictly technical
subject, and only rarely does the voice of an evolutionist
penetrate to the general public. The last such voice was
Teilhard de Chardin's, but it arrived on the wings of a
legend, and its impact was due more to its poetic ring than
to its content—a mystery wrapped in metaphor. Professor
Alister Hardy speaks in a more sober voice; his message, too,
has a religious core, but this is religion stripped of dogma and
wrapped in hard empirical fact. The provocative sub-title of
his book, 'A Restatement of Evolution Theory and its
Relation to the Spirit of Man', defines precisely what it sets
out to do.

His challenge to the prevailing orthodox theory of evolution is contained in two revolutionary proposals. The first is
that 'the emphasis in the present-day view must be false';
that the dominant causative factor of evolutionary progress
is *not* the selective pressure of the environment but the
initiative of the living organism, 'the restless, exploring and

---

[*] Sir Alister Hardy's Gifford Lectures were published in two volumes:
The Living Stream (1965) and *The Divine Flame* (1966). I reviewed the first
in the *Sunday Times* (14.11.1965), the second in the *New Scientist*
(29.12.1966).

perceiving animal that discovers new ways of living, new sources of food . . . giving us the lines of runners, climbers, burrowers, swimmers and conquerors of the air'.

To the layman this dynamic view of the journey from amoeba to man may sound almost self-evident; to the contemporary biologist it sounds like sheer Lamarckian heresy. For the last hundred years, the theorists of evolution have been fighting an embittered civil war of Lamarckian Roundheads versus Darwinist Cavaliers. The actual dispute was of a complex, technical character; but it was highly charged with metaphysical, emotional and even political implications (in the Soviet Union the Cavaliers were summarily sent to labour camps under Stalin, and the survivors summarily rehabilitated under Khrushchev, an episode known as the 'Lysenko affair'). The main issue, over-simplified and crammed into a nutshell, is this. Lamarck believed that the adaptive modifications of an animal's physique and behaviour, which it acquires to cope more effectively with its environment, are transmitted by heredity to the offspring ('inheritance of acquired characteristics'). The giraffe strains his neck and forelegs to reach the foliage of tall trees; his offspring benefits from the parents' experience by being born with longer neck and forelegs. This would provide a reassuring and sensible view of evolution as the cumulative result of learning-from-experience, but unfortunately the evidence shows that the genes of heredity are not directly affected by anything which animal or man experiences in his lifetime; as far as heredity is concerned, it all seems wasted.

Neo-Darwinism, on the other hand, teaches a kind of monkey-at-the-typewriter theory of evolution. Mutations— changes in the molecular structure of genes—occur at random, unrelated to the animal's needs; most of them have deleterious effects, but the few lucky hits are preserved because they happen to confer some small advantage on the individual; and 'given time, anything at all will turn up'. 'The hoary objection,' wrote Sir Julian Huxley, 'of the improbability of an eye or a hand or a brain being evolved by "blind chance" has lost its force.'

In fact it has not. The theory, as it stands, leaves a number of basic phenomena unexplained, and it seems unlikely that it will ever be able to explain them. No biologist can doubt that random-mutation-cum-natural-selection plays an important part in evolution; the question is whether this is the whole truth, or even the most important part of the truth. Sir Alister emphatically denies this. Let me explain his point by a witty example of his own.

In recent years some bright tits discovered the uses of opening milk bottles—first those with cardboard tops, then those with metal tops; a discovery which soon spread 'apparently through copying right through the tit population of Europe'. Now if milk bottles were living organisms, and a species of tits specialised on them for food, then in due time only those 'bottles' which had thicker 'caps' would survive, and natural selection would lead to even thicker caps—but also to tits with 'more specialised tin-opener-like beaks for dealing with them'.

The evolution of thick-capped 'bottles' illustrates the 'passive', Darwinian type of evolutionary mechanism (selective pressure of predators). But the evolution of the tits is a quite different story, because the birds took the initiative, discovered a new skill which, spreading by imitation, became part of their repertory of habits; and the lucky mutation (or reshuffling) of genes came only afterwards, giving a kind of genetic sanction to the discovery. The pioneer work, so to speak, was achieved by learning and insight; the monkey got busy on his typewriter only later on, and he no longer has to write a Sonnet, but merely go on trying until he hits a pre-specified key.

The example is imaginary, but supported by a vast array of fact. Thus, for instance, one of 'Darwin's finches' in the Galapagos pecks holes or crevices in the tree-bark, then seizes a twig in his beak and pokes with it inside for insects. Reminding us of the fantastic variety of beaks and their uses, Sir Alister asks: 'Can it really be maintained that it is *more likely* that random mutations force these different groups of birds to their different modes of life, rather than that they developed different habits and that such differences in feeding led gradually to beaks better and better adapted to their ways of life?'

I shall not attempt to explain in detail why this conception puts a new face with a new look on the phenomena of evolution. The idea is not entirely new: it was proposed by Baldwin and Lloyd Morgan at the turn of the century (under the name of 'organic selection') and was experimentally demonstrated by Professor Waddington (who calls it 'genetic assimilation'). But it is one thing to recognise the existence of a phenomenon as a subsidiary effect of minor importance—as the orthodox theorists do—and quite another to develop its scientific and philosophic implications —as Sir Alister does—and to claim it as the dominant factor in the evolutionary process. Revolutions in science are sometimes due not to the discovery of new facts but to a shift of emphasis.

The second of the proposals that I mentioned, and related to the first, is put forward in a breathtaking excursion into 'natural theology'. The author discusses first the evidence for the existence of telepathy which—as one among a growing minority of scientists—he regards as conclusive. He considers it to be unlikely that such a remarkable quality should be confined to a small number of human beings, and more likely that it is widespread in the animal kingdom—something akin to Jung's collective unconscious. Such a shared 'psychic blueprint' might, he suggests, explain some of the basic difficulties of evolution theory—particularly those relating to the emergence of complex but uniform behaviour-patterns in primitive animals. It may also be a means of subterranean communication between man and the *anima mundi* of 'natural theology'. These ideas are only sketched out in a summary way at the end of the first of the two series of Gifford Lectures on which the present volume is based;

their detailed consideration must wait for the next volume.

But even this brief foretaste shows that they are scandalous speculations by the standards of the *Zeitgeist*; it is fortunate that their author is not a starry-eyed metaphysician, but a Professor of Zoology at Oxford and one of the foremost authorities in his field, speaking with the learned, gentle voice of a snake in the grass of Darwinian orthodoxy. My only criticism of the book is that it does not mention one of the major missing bits in the jigsaw puzzle of current evolution theory: the 'internal' selection of mutations through selective and regulative control on the molecular, chromosomal and cellular level. To readers interested in the field I would recommend L. L. Whyte's *Internal Factors in Evolution* (Tavistock, 1965).

2   *The divine flame**

In reviewing the first series of Professor Hardy's Gifford Lectures, published last year, I wrote that he was speaking as a snake in the grass of neo-Darwinian orthodoxy. In the present, second series, the snake's gentle whisper has changed into a siren's song, intended to beguile unwary travellers to the rocky island of Natural Theology. The correct scientific attitude is of course to stuff wax into one's ears.

This, however, is made more difficult by Hardy's own insistence on a rigorously empirical approach, in keeping with Lord Gifford's bequest that the lectures should treat Natural Theology 'as a strictly natural science, without relevance or reliance upon any . . . so-called miraculous revelation'. On the negative side, the author certainly conforms to the injunction by rejecting any orthodox dogma, including the Resurrection, and doubting whether, if Jesus were living today, he would call himself a Christian (p.

* See footnote on p. 166.

218). On the positive side he follows several convergent lines of approach.

The first is biological. He quotes Polanyi's 'tacit knowledge' by unverbalised intuitions, and Waddington's thesis that man is of necessity highly receptive to indoctrination, an animal that 'goes in for believing'. This chapter, however, is incomplete in itself, and should be read in conjunction with Lectures VI to X of the first series.

Next he turns to the evidence which social anthropologists (from Durkheim to Evans-Pritchard) have to offer, and concludes: 'The overriding impression from all these studies of the religions of primitive man from all over the world is that he is conscious of being in touch with some Power which appears to be outside and beyond the individual self and from which he can receive grace: help in the conduct of his life and a sense of renewed vitality' (p. 80). He finds these conclusions sustained by the psychological evidence in William James's *The Varieties Of Religious Experience*, in the works of Jung, and other psychologists. As for Freud, he concedes that man's image of a Father in Heaven may be strongly coloured by love and fear of his father on Earth; but the crucial point for Hardy is 'that the equation of the Freudian super-ego with the idea of Divinity cannot be complete, and does not destroy the reality of the spiritual experience'. In a similar way, sexual feelings and sado-masochistic aberrations may get mixed up with mysticism; but they are by-products, not its essence. The essence, in Hardy's view, is the irreducible experience of what Richard Otto called the numinous, the *mysterium tremendum et fascinans*; and the channels of communication between man and the numinous are extra-sensory perception (which he considers to be proven beyond doubt) and contemplative prayer. If these postulates are true, Hardy concludes, they ought to be confirmable by experiment; and in his last lecture he announces the founding of a research unit for exactly this purpose at Manchester College, Oxford, of which he is an Honorary President. 'It is the College in which, in its early days in the eighteenth century, such men as Joseph Priestley and John Dalton combined with brilliance both scientific achievement and a deep spiritual faith' (p. 244).

Whatever one's attitude, one cannot be but deeply moved by this act of faith. It is beyond this reviewer's competence to decide whether God exists. All he can do is to state his personal bias: that only a fool would deny dimensions of reality unknowable to man, which may add up to a coherent whole; but that only a saint would attribute to it the qualities of benevolence and love. For all we know the *anima mundi* might be a Portuguese man-of-war. Professor Hardy's God certainly bears no anthropomorphic features; but also shows no trace of cruelty. The most obvious criticism to be levelled against his book by believers and unbelievers alike is that, except for a few passing mentions, it evades the crucial question of evil.

Even so, it makes immensely stimulating reading. For we are all susceptible to the siren's song, whether we admit it or not; and that is perhaps the strongest argument in favour of Alister Hardy's point of view.

The Patient's Dilemma

Fringe Medicine by Brian Inglis*

This book will cause a healthy scandal. It is a frontal attack on the narrow-minded orthodoxy of the medical establishment and a spirited defence of the unorthodox methods practised on its fringes. Among these the author includes nature cures and herbalism; homoeopathy, osteopathy and chiropractics; acupuncture; psychotherapy and hypnosis; faith healing and radiesthesia.

Any writer who ventures into these troubled waters must keep on a precarious course between the Scylla of rigid dogmatism and the Charybdis of gullibility; Brian Inglis seems at times to sail perilously close to the second. Thus he argues in defence of acupuncture that it has been 'the standard form of medical treatment in China for five thousand years', and he defends dowsing and radiesthesia by referring to 'the sheer weight of anecdotal evidence'. But a belief can persist for five thousand years and nevertheless be a delusion; and the weight of anecdotal evidence for witches riding on brooms is overwhelming. Mr. Inglis is too generous in bestowing the benefit of doubt even in cases where negative certainty leaves no room for doubt—e.g. the de la Warr 'box' or the late Wilhelm Reich's Orgonomy.

* Reviewed in *The Observer*, 1.3.1964.

These are minor faults, but unfortunately they will provide welcome ammunition for the defenders of the Citadel, and detract from the power of the author's main argument—which is of vital importance to us all. I cannot attempt to summarise it, merely to mention a few salient points.

Medicine became an exact science only about a century ago, when Pasteur established the germ theory of disease against the bitter opposition of the profession. But the high hopes which accompanied its spectacular successes in combating infectious diseases yielded to a more sober outlook when it became evident that the methods which had led to the disappearance of some of the old scourges of humanity were less effective when applied to others. Ulcers, asthma, coronary thrombosis, disorders of the circulatory and digestive systems, instead of going out, seemed actually on the increase—not to mention psychiatric disorders. Other factors contributed to the sobering process. Some of the new wonder drugs turned out to have side effects of varying severity. Others caused the emergence of new, drug-resisting strains of micro-organisms. Voices from both inside and outside the profession began to call attention to the risk that the all-out war on micro-organisms may upset the overall balance of nature by a process analogous to the indiscriminate use of insecticides. But in this case the ecological upheaval was taking place inside the human organism: 80 per cent of the micro-fauna which inhabits our bowels is still unknown; and drastic interference with this fauna may undermine the body's natural resistance.

By the 1950s the work of Selye and others had shown that the chief culprit in some diseases was not the foreign invader, but the organisms' inability to cope with him—an impairment due to a variety of causes, but surprisingly often to mental stress. Experiment showed that even rats put under emotional strain died of small doses of poison which, under normal conditions, they would have thrown off; 'the implication being that human illnesses usually attributed to germs or poisons ought properly to be blamed on the stress which allows or encourages the germs to proliferate'.

Equally surprising was the discovery of a phenomenon of the opposite kind—the relief or cure of organic symptoms by the purely psychological action of so-called placebos. These are inactive dummy pills which physicians have been administering from time immemorial to lift the patient's morale (placebo = 'I will please'); but recently they have been used as experimental controls to determine whether the beneficial effect of a new drug is due to its intrinsic merits or to suggestion and auto-suggestion.

Three years ago I reported in these columns on experimental work in the United States which suggested that at least one-third of the total hospital population are 'placebo reactors' who will react to dummy pills as if they were what they believed them to be. In 1962 the *British Medical Journal* reported on a test carried out with patients suffering from angina pectoris. Different groups of patients were given either one of two potent drugs or a tranquilliser or a placebo; and 'more patients reacted favourably to the placebo than to any of the drugs'.

These examples could be multiplied; the upshot is, in Mr. Inglis's words, 'not that these drugs have no merit, but that placebo effect is a much more powerful and widespread component of treatment than is realised'. In other words, suggestion and auto-suggestion involving both physician and patient play an incomparably greater part in every form of therapy than orthodox medicine would admit.

There is nothing very new in this. Hypnosis can make a person drunk on water, cause blisters to rise as a reaction to imaginary burns, cure warts, suppress the pain in dental surgery and even in major operations. Yet the hypnotic state is merely an extreme form of that suggestibility of the unconscious mind to which we all are normally prone; and the effects of which do not stop at some imaginary frontier between 'psyche' and 'soma' or between 'functional' and 'organic' disorders.

That frontier is crumbling, and the psychosomatic approach has come to stay. That stomach ulcers can be caused by mental stress has become a commonplace; the suggestion that even malignant growths may be of psychogenic origin still seems fantastic. Yet nearly ten years ago the eminent surgeon Sir William Heneage Ogilvie at Guy's asked the startling question: 'We all have cancer at forty-eight. What is the force which keeps it in check in the great majority of us?'—and went on to suggest that it was intimately related to psychological factors: 'The happy man never gets cancer.'

This new outlook unavoidably implies a more open-minded attitude to 'fringe medicine'. Mr. Inglis defines it as forms of therapy which, though widely varied, all rely on the *vis medicatrix naturae*, on man's natural recuperative powers, in preference to drugs or surgery—powers which 'all fringe practitioners agree can be speeded up sometimes to an astonishing degree by suitable stimuli'. And the simplest and oldest of such stimuli is suggestion *cum* auto-suggestion. It enters into such half-empirical, half folklore-begotten practices as herbalism; it is probably the most (and sometimes the only) effective factor in the various techniques of manipulation and the laying of hands; and it provides the rationale for Mr. Inglis's over-indulgent attitude towards the mumbo-jumbo of the 'pendulum' or the de la Warr 'box'. If the mumbo-jumbo works, he argues, then why not?—provided, of course, that there is no dangerous condition present requiring some specific intervention. And if it works, it does so because the practitioner himself believes in his method, and his faith is transferred to the patient. So powerful are the unconscious forces involved in this kind of transference, that drug-testing experiments are now carried out according to the 'double-blind method', where doctors and nurses themselves are not allowed to know whether they are handing out a drug or a dummy pill—to eliminate the faith-healing factor.

Witch doctors have always known the power of suggestion:

this ancient knowledge, temporarily lost during the age of mechanistic science, has acquired a new urgency in the light of the modern psychosomatic approach.

The implications are obvious in so far as the medical profession is concerned. But they are less obvious from the patient's point of view. It we are all placebo reactors in one way or another, does not this knowledge destroy that very faith which is half the therapy?

The answer to the apparent dilemma is that all effective suggestion operates on unconscious levels. What the patient has to learn is to be guided in the choice of his physician not by the nature of his complaint, but by the intuitive trust or distrust which the physician's personality inspires in him. Once the *rapport* is established, even if scepticism or doubt survives on the surface of the mind, the benevolent magic will set to work on levels beyond their reach. And whatever the method of the therapy, the essence of that magic is always the silent injunction: 'Patient, cure thyself.'

The Patient as a Guinea Pig

Human Guinea Pigs—Experimentation on Man by
M. H. Pappworth.*

The author of *Human Guinea Pigs*, a consultant physician, has
been for many years engaged in a crusade against irresponsible medical experimentation on human beings. Crusaders
tend to become obsessed with their cause, and there are
indications that Dr. Pappworth is no exception—although
he avoids emotionalism, utters his *j'accuse* in dry, restrained
terms, and even resorts to the conventional understatements
of his profession ('symptoms of discomfort' for 'howling with
pain').

Nevertheless his book is liable to spread alarm and
suspicion among lay-readers, and particularly among
prospective hospital patients. This is the unavoidable side-
effect of any work that exposes the fallibility—or *hubris*, or
mercenariness—of the medical world. Faith in the omni-
science of the medicine man is an essential element in all
healing, and he who shatters that faith assumes a responsibility towards the patient comparable to the physician's. A
semi-educated person, superficially browsing through the
more lurid pages of Dr. Pappworth's book might easily
jump to the conclusion that to go to a hospital for a minor

* Reviewed in the *New Statesman*, 26.5.1967.

operation is equivalent to being lured to the island of Dr. Moreau and vivisected by a team of researchers with steely eyes over white masks.

The book has indeed a gruesome effect on the general reader unacquainted with the techniques of modern surgery, who has never watched a major operation, and would probably faint—as novices are proverbially wont to do—at the sight of the gory mess revealed by the first incision. With this warning in mind, watch your reactions while reading the following description—typical of many others—of an experiment performed in a British hospital in 1942 on sixteen children, aged eleven to sixteen, and one adult aged twenty:*

> The experiment consisted in passing a catheter, under X-ray control, via the main arm vein into the subclavian vein of the chest, thence into the superior veina cava, thence into the right atrium of the heart, and so into the pulmonary artery. At the same time, a tightly fitting face mask and nose clip were applied to each child's face, so that samples of air breathed out could be collected for analysis. After blood samples had been taken from the heart (through the catheter) and pressure recordings within the heart were obtained, the children were made to 'cycle' on a special machine, and they did this with a cardiac catheter and face mask remaining in position.

But before waxing indignant, we should be aware that cardiac catheterisation—pushing a hollow tube through a vein in a limb into the heart, and through the heart into other circuits—has become quite common practice in modern surgery. The surgeon who invented the technique repeatedly performed it on himself in public demonstrations, and so did other teachers of clinical medicine. The vein (or artery) through which the catheter passes is insensitive; and the only slight pain involved is caused by the piercing of the

* It should be pointed out that Dr. Pappworth meticulously provides the names of the hospitals and doctors involved in all experiments quoted by him, and gives references to the medical journals in which the results were quoted.

skin to get the catheter into the vein (done, if necessary, under local anaesthetics). Similar considerations apply to most of the experiments on human subjects reported in the book—including, for instance, one performed on '113 new-born infants, aged one to seventy-seven hours, of whom twenty-six had been premature births'. The authors (of the Department of Pediatrics, University of California) report that 'when, without prior premedication, a catheter was passed via the umbilical artery into the infant's aorta, "with few exceptions the infants appeared to be completely content"'.

But when the macabre aura surrounding these experiments is dispelled, and emotionalism bred by ignorance discounted, there remains a hard core of cases in Dr. Pappworth's list where his criticisms seem to be fully justified. This applies particularly to some experiments carried out on children, on pregnant women, mental defectives, on patients before and after an operation, and on those with incurable diseases; and to a lesser extent on prisoner volunteers. Theoretically, no experiment can be performed without the patient's (or in the case of minors, the parents') consent. In practice, the con-senting patient (or guardian or next-of-kin) is often quite unable to assess the risks and amount of suffering involved in the experiment. In addition, he might be exposed to subtle, or not so subtle, means of persuasion and psychological pressure—the bulk of the experimental 'material' is pro-vided by the poorer strata of the hospital population and by prisoners (in Victorian days they were mostly 'orphans, foundlings and criminals').

The worst cases, however, are those where the distinction between medical therapy and medical research is inad-vertently or deliberately blurred by the physician in charge. A medical research experiment is usually defined as some-thing done to the patient which is of no direct therapeutic (or diagnostic) value to his own sickness, but is meant to benefit 'the progress of science' or mankind at large. It is this definition which draws the line between patient and guinea pig. Dr. Pappworth reports several cases where patients were subjected to operations or medications which they thought to be intended to cure them, but which had in fact nothing to do with their illness. These, of course, are totally indefensible practices, however lofty the motivation behind them. And not infrequently (as some eminent clinicians have pointed out) even the motives are not all that lofty, but excessive zeal or a craving for renown.

In the concluding chapters of his book the author proposes Parliamentary legislation to control human experimentation, in accord with certain ethical principles. Any proposed experiment would have to be endorsed by a Consultation Committee (which must include a lay member, 'preferably a lawyer'). Each committee should be responsible to the General Medical Council, which in its turn would be answerable to Parliament. All this sounds admirable in theory, yet Dr. Pappworth himself admits that as the result of a bureaucratic machinery of this sort 'research, in so far as it depends on medical experiment, would be substantially slowed up'. In view of the notorious conservativism of the medical profession in general, and particularly of those of its members who have attained to eminence in official positions, one wonders how slow the slowed-up process would become. It seems fairly certain that Edward Jenner would never have obtained the consent of his Regional Board Committee (including a nice, elderly solicitor) to inoculate an eight-year-old boy with matter from the cow-pox vesicles on the hands of a milk-maid, to prove that it conferred immunity against smallpox—and thus to liberate mankind from the worst killer of previous centuries.

It all boils down to the old, old question under what circumstances and to what extent the end justifies the means. An Act of Statute, as proposed by the author, could hardly be expected to solve that problem; it could only be justified as a desperate measure in the case of urgent necessity. Dr. Pappworth evidently believes that such a necessity exists; in his preface he says that 'the ethical problems arising from human experimentation have become one of the cardinal issues of our time'. This is one of the few overstatements in his book, but it is a monumental one. A few pages later, he quotes from a letter he wrote in 1963 to the *British Medical Journal*: 'The majority of those engaged in clinical research act with the highest moral integrity, but an expanding minority resort to unethical and probably illegal practices.' The crucial question is whether the irresponsible minority is really 'expanding' or not. In 1963 it may have been. But since then the effective public protests of people like Dr. Beecher in Harvard, and Dr. Pappworth himself, have to a considerable extent altered the situation; and I think that most research workers who are in a position to know what is going on would confirm that the horrors described in Dr. Pappworth's book are on the wane. The pendulum may even be moving towards the opposite extreme—as the over-cautious attitude of the American Food and Drug Administration seems to indicate.

Human Guinea Pigs is a book to be pondered by the profession. There is less point in recommending it to the general public—which has other 'cardinal issues' to worry about.

Daughter to Stalin

Twenty Letters to a Friend. By Svetlana Alliluyeva.*

After the flourish of trumpets, one was prepared for almost anything—a new Tolstoy or Kafka or an authentic Borgia diary. But one was certainly not prepared for the voice of this nice, homely woman, treating us to nice, homely reflections, such as: 'In our century of sudden changes and rapid transformations, strong family ties and the continuity of tradition have a very pleasing effect wherever they are still found to exist.'

This passage, with a number of others in a similar vein, has been excised from the English version of the book. The translator has also eliminated expletives, adjectives and whole paragraphs of patchy purple. The result is wholly beneficial from the point of view of readability. On the other hand, the German edition (which I read first) sounds in places like a serial from a popular woman's magazine, but seems closer to the original and to reflect more faithfully the author's personality: that of a conventional bourgeois house-wife, strong-willed but with a warm Russian heart, given to occasional gushing, and without a trace of personal vanity.

Up to the age of sixteen Svetlana worshipped little Papa with his big kisses, and also the numerous uncles, aunts, in-

* Reviewed in the *Sunday Times*, 1.10.1967.

laws, nannies, babushkas and friends of the family—without apparently noticing that uncles, aunts and closest friends one after the other turned out to be enemies of the people and disappeared from the face of the earth. Only at sixteen did she experience her 'first feeble stirrings of doubt' (p. 182).

The occasion was just one more disappearance: that of her sister-in-law, Yulia, the wife of Yakov Dzhugashvili, Stalin's older son (by his first wife). In 1941, Yakov, an artillery officer, was captured with his unit by the Germans (and was eventually shot after Stalin had refused an offer to exchange him against a high-ranking German officer (pp. 173–74)). When it became known that Yakov was a prisoner-of-war, his wife was arrested and jailed for two years 'under the terrible statute providing for punishment of relatives of those who have been taken prisoners' (p. 196). But Papa also confided to Svetlana his suspicion that Yulia had somehow 'tricked' her husband and contrived his capture (p. 172). The episode merely illustrates how far Stalin's paranoia had progressed by that time, for he was not at all fond of Yakov:

> In his eyes Yakov could do nothing right . . . In despair over the attitude of my father, who refused to have anything to do with him, Yakov [at the age of twenty] went to the kitchen of our Kremlin apartment and shot himself. Luckily he was only wounded. The bullet went right through. My father made fun of him and liked to sneer: 'Ha! He couldn't even shoot straight!' (p. 111).

But Svetlana's mother, Nadezhda Alliluyeva, could. After a public humiliation by her husband, she rushed home, shot herself with a tiny pistol, and died. Svetlana was at the time six; but she only discovered ten years later, by reading an article in a foreign magazine, that her mother had died by her own hand.

Nadezhda's son, Vasily, five years Svetlana's senior, did not fare much better. Bullied throughout his life by his father, he became an alcoholic and died at the age of forty-one. As for the fate of the varied uncles, aunts and in-laws,

it is difficult not to be reminded of the Ten Little Nigger
Boys. Svetlana summed it up:

> You are probably worn out by now, my friend, with the
> countless deaths I have been telling you about. But did I know
> a single person whose life turned out well? It was as though
> my father was at the centre of a black circle, and anyone who
> ventured inside vanished or perished or was destroyed in one
> way or another (p. 233) .... When I asked him what my aunts
> were guilty of, he told me, 'They talked a lot, they knew too
> much and they talked too much, and it helped our enemies.'
> He was bitter, as bitter as he could be against the whole world.
> He saw enemies everywhere. It had reached the point of being
> pathological, of persecution mania. . . . 'You yourself make
> anti-Soviet statements,' he told me one day angrily and in
> complete earnest. I did not try to object or ask where he got
> that from (p. 207).

If Papa had lived on, Svetlana too might have been
swallowed up by the black circle. Just before he died—in the
absence of his old physician, who had looked after him for
many years and was now in jail on a charge of conspiring
with Western intelligence to murder Soviet leaders:

> he suddenly opened his eyes and cast a glance over everyone in
> the room. It was a terrible glance, insane or perhaps angry and
> full of fear of death and the unfamiliar faces of the doctors bent
> over him. The glance swept over everyone in a second. Then
> something incomprehensible and terrible happened that to this
> day I can't forget and don't understand. He suddenly lifted his
> left hand as though he were pointing to something up above
> and bringing down a curse on us all.

Yet when at last he was dead, and the servants and body-
guards came to say goodbye:

> They went up to the bed silently and wept . . . They wiped
> their tears away as children do with their hands and sleeves and
> handkerchiefs . . . All these men and women who were servants
> of my father loved him . . . They loved and respected him for
> the most ordinary human qualities, those qualities of which
> servants are the best judges of all (pp. 19–20).

And as a finishing touch:

> He had not once found time to see five of his eight grand-
> children. Yet even the grandchildren who never saw him loved
> him and love him still. During those days, when he found
> peace at last on his deathbed, and his face became beautiful
> and serene, I felt my heart breaking from grief and love (p. 17).

A novelist could not create a more convincing example of
the ambivalence of human emotions; and the contradictory
statements caused by this ambivalence do not detract from
the value of Svetlana's book—on the contrary, they confirm
its authenticity. But though authentic and sincere beyond
doubt, the question remains whether the book contributes
anything new to our knowledge of history.

It certainly contains no startling revelations. It sheds no
new light on the purges, show trials, absurd indictments and
incredible confessions. They are mentioned only by indirect
allusions (the Stalin-Hitler Pact, the rape of Poland, are not
mentioned at all). Svetlana's explanation of the horrors of
Stalin's regime is astonishingly naive: they had been en-
gineered by the villainous Beria, who 'cast a spell' (p. 149)
on Papa and used him as a tool for his own diabolic designs.
When she speaks of Beria, Svetlana loses all restraint and
reverts to the familiar invectives of the Party jargon which
she otherwise abhors: he is a 'monster', 'utterly degenerate',
'the embodiment of Oriental perfidy, flattery and hypocrisy'
—and, needless to say, 'a born spy and provocateur' who
had been in the service of Armenian nationalists.

In other words, Svetlana has found a scapegoat for her
father's sins. Psychologically this is understandable and
pardonable; historically it is, of course, complete nonsense.
She herself seems to be partly aware of this: 'In a good many
things my father and Beria were guilty together. I am not
trying to shift the blame from one to the other' (p. 149). Yet
this is precisely what she does, by pretending, for instance,
that Stalin himself believed in the fantastic confessions extracted from his old comrades: 'What my father didn't

realise was that in the cellars of the Secret Police, X, Y and Z could be made to testify to anything' (p. 86). If Stalin did not realise this, he was the only one who didn't in the whole of Russia.

Thus the *Twenty Letters* offer the historian neither new facts of importance nor reliable interpretations. Their value lies elsewhere: in providing background, atmosphere, local colour—or, one should rather say, the absence of colour. The picture that emerges of life in the Kremlin apartment and in the country *dachas*, seen through a young woman's eyes, is of an utterly depressing drabness, greyness and banality. Stalin's reign was one of the goriest episodes in history; yet one gets the impression that even the blood of the victims looked grey in the gutters of the execution cellars.

'He was difficult to talk to,' she writes of a visit to Stalin in 1947. 'Strange as it may seem, we had nothing to say to one another . . . In the evening we looked at old pre-war movies like *Volga-Volga* and films by Chaplin.

'The whole crowd would come for dinner, Beria, Malenkov, Zhdanov, Bulganin and the rest. I found it dull and exhausting to sit three or four hours at the table listening to the same old stories as if there were no news and nothing whatever going on in the world! It made me dead tired and I would go off to bed' (p. 201).

Her last visit took place five years later.

'. . . We sat at the table as usual, and the usual people were present [Beria, Malenkov, Bulganin, Mikoyan, Khrushchev]. There was the usual talk, the same old jokes I had been hearing for years . . . Everything was the same as ever at the table —not a single new word. It was as though the outside world didn't exist' (p. 217 f).

In her Preface Svetlana wrote that the aim of her book was 'to bear witness'. She is unavoidably a confused witness, who is trying hard to be objective, but cannot escape her ambivalent feelings, and cannot help coming up with rationalisations and excuses—not for the system, but for poor, bad, mad, little Papa, whom she considers to have been a product

187

of the system. In a recent interview she was asked: 'Would you say that if your father had not existed there would have been another Stalin?'

Her short reply was: 'I believe so.'

This belief in historical determinism, and in man as a playball of its blind forces, if it were true, would provide the ultimate vindication, not only of Stalin but of all the large and small fry who have brought harm to mankind. It is a source of strength to totalitarian ideology; and it is our weakness that though we reject it, we have not found a complete answer to it.

Mistress to Picasso

Life With Picasso. By Françoise Gilot and Carlton Lake*

Picasso picked up Françoise Gilot when he was sixty-two and she a rather prim virgin of twenty-one. The year was 1943; she was dining out with friends at a Left Bank restaurant in occupied Paris, 'wearing a green turban that covered much of my brow and cheeks'; Picasso, also in the company of friends, sat at the next table. During dinner he kept acting up for her benefit and finally came over to her table with a bowl of cherries, and managed to get introduced by her escort, an actor whom he knew only by sight. On learning that Françoise was a budding painter, he invited her to his studio.

That was how it began. It ended ten years later, when Françoise walked out on him and packed their two children and her bags into a taxi, to drive to the station at Vallauris. The farewell scene was brief: 'He shouted "*Merde!*" and went back into the house.'

In fact, the whole affair was doomed from the outset, as both Picasso's and Mlle Gilot's friends knew. It could even be called a tragi-comedy, in the classic sense, where the accent is on the first half of the word. Picasso not only loved to act the tragic clown; he did it compulsively, so that it seems

* Reviewed in *The Observer*, 3.3.1965.

189

impossible to draw a line between the person and the act:

> Almost every morning as Pablo lathered his face for shaving, he would trace with a finger in the billowing cream the enormous caricatured lips, the suggestion of a question mark over the eyebrows, and the path of tears oozing out of each eye —the stigmata of the professional clown. His make-up complete, he would begin to gesticulate and grimace with an intensity that made it clear that this was not only a game he enjoyed but, at the same time, something more.

Clowns like cruel games, but their cruelty has the innocence of the dear little ones pulling out the fly's wings. Olga, Picasso's first wife, who had become deranged in middle-age, was persecuting Françoise: she would follow her about in the streets, shouting threats and abuse, or pinch and scratch her when Françoise was fumbling for her house-keys with her baby son in her arms. One day she was resting on the beach with her arms stretched behind her, 'when Olga came up in back of me and with her high heels began walking over my hands. Pablo saw what she was up to and roared with laughter . . . Finally I grabbed Olga's foot and gave it a twist and she went flat on her face in the sand.' Picasso enjoyed such scenes vastly.

He also enjoyed counting and recounting the five to six thousand pounds' worth of bank-notes which he kept in an old red-leather trunk 'so that he'd always have the cash for a package of cigarettes'; and he enjoyed boasting of his membership of the Communist Party. He enjoyed hoarding things and could not bear throwing any object away—not even empty matchboxes, or old clothes which had turned into transparent spider-webs after the moth had eaten all the wool away, and only the buckram and tailor's stitches had survived. It was not miserliness, but another compulsion. He could not part with anything he possessed, but he derived no pleasure from its possession. His art treasures were stored away—some in the vaults of a bank and some in an uninhabited apartment which he never visited, in the rue de la Boétie, where old newspapers, magazines and junk filled the dusty rooms nearly to the ceiling; the cave of Ali Baba, Françoise called it.

She soon discovered that this mania to hang on to any useless, discarded object derived from a powerful superstition. When Françoise gave away an old jacket of Picasso's to the gardener, he got into such a rage that they almost broke up ('It's dreadful. It's monstrous. You want me to be transformed into that ugly old man? . . . Well, if that is your intention, I'm leaving immediately'). According to ancient lore, when some intimate possession of a person—clothes, hair, nail trimmings—falls into the hands of someone else, he acquires power over that person. Accordingly 'Pablo would go for months needing a haircut, but was unable to bring himself to walk into a barber-shop. The longer they grew, the more anguished he became.' For a while Françoise had to cut his hair, or he did it himself 'with most unsightly results'. Finally he met a Spanish barber called Arias who could be trusted not to engage in black magic with the severed locks. 'From then on Arias used to come whenever a haircut could be postponed no longer. I never knew what happened to the hair and don't to this day.'

Above all he hoarded his women:

> Pablo's many stories and reminiscences about Olga and Marie-Thérèse and Dora Maar, as well as their continuing presence just offstage in our own life together, gradually made me realise that he had a kind of Bluebeard complex that made him want to cut off the heads of all the women he had collected in his little private museum. But he didn't cut the heads entirely off. He preferred to have life go on and to have all those women who had shared his life at one moment or another still letting out little peeps and cries of joy or pain and making a few gestures like disjointed dolls, just to prove there was some life left in them, that it hung by a thread, and that he held the other end of the thread.

Art dealers are no saints, but some of them Picasso almost managed to turn into martyrs; the cat-and-mouse games he played with these tough characters make one feel rather sorry for them. But for Françoise, who stood it for ten years, one does not feel pity, only admiration—and just occasionally a touch of irritation caused by her many flawless virtues. She was able to stand up to that capering centaur with the deadly hoofs because of her penetrating insight into his character—and into his work; herself a painter of considerable achievement, her unqualified admiration for his genius had an added dimension of depth. But above all, she was able to hold her own because, the headstrong daughter of a headstrong father, she had benefited from an education of Victorian rigour. *Françoise:* 'All my life I had been warned away from public displays of emotion.' *Picasso:* 'When I shout at you and say disagreeable things, it's to toughen you up . . . I'd like you to get angry, shout, and carry on, but you don't. I'd like just once to see you spill your guts out on the table, laugh, cry—play *my* game.'

This about sums it up. But incompatibility of temperament would be a facile explanation. He had lived with a variety of women with a variety of temperaments, and the outcome had been much the same. The incompatibility is not between the characters, but between the temperament of genius and the institution of monogamy. God knows, it is a brittle affair even for ordinary mortals; in the case of geniuses of the Picasso type it reduces itself to absurdity.

The book demonstrates this almost with the conclusiveness of a mathematical proof. So much goodwill on both sides, and all in vain. 'When you came into my life it was like the opening of a window,' Picasso told her at the beginning. Yet slowly, inexorably, the window shut close. The last impression that remains with the reader is gratitude that he was allowed to press his nose against the pane and watch the unique figure behind it, in shorts and striped sailor's shirt, performing high jinks in his solitude; but above all to watch him at work with oils, charcoal, clay, glazes, acids, etching tools, turning a pair of rusty bicycle handles into the horns of a goat, transforming Françoise into the *Femme-Fleur*, absorbed in his painstaking magic.

Books of the Years?

The annual game, in which a number of *literati* are invited by certain Sunday papers to name, and comment on, their favourite books published that year, is a standing feature of the Christmas season. I have collected, as a curiosity, my own selections, published (in *The Observer* and the *Sunday Times*) over the last twelve years. The question mark in the title indicates awareness of the fact that the predictions of lasting survival (or at least resurrection as a paperback) implied in each choice are as fallible as the astrologers' predictions published in the more popular papers at the same time of year.

1955 William Golding's *The Inheritors* (Faber) gave me the impression of an earthquake in the petrified forests of the English novel. I shall not mention its subject because to those who have not read it, it may sound like science fiction, though it is the opposite: a beautifully written psychological novel about very unusual people. The death of Lok is the most moving scene I have read for a long time, in spite of the hero's peculiarity of living mainly by the sense of smell.

Knut Hamsun's classic *Pan* was published in an excellent new translation by the Artemis Press, who promise a complete edition of the works of that half-forgotten giant.

Equally welcome is the recent omnibus edition of James

Fenimore Cooper's *The Leatherstocking Saga* (Collins). I read it thirty-odd years ago in my native Hungarian, in which the hero's name read 'Börharisnya', and I am still convinced that that is his *real* name. To the nostalgic adult reader, the Saga has a kind of delightful unreadability.

1956   Novel of the year: *Pincher Martin*, by William Golding (Faber). Mr. Golding's first novel was about children on a desert island reverting to the Stone Age; his second about the ousting of Neanderthal man by *homo sapiens*; his third is simply about the Condition of Man, and the stage has been reduced from island and cave to a single naked rock in the ocean. Mr. Golding seems to be engaged in re-claiming for the novel a kind of lost property which had passed into the possession of the hacks of science fiction: I mean cosmic awareness. He has both the spiritual and technical equipment to succeed.

Bubble of the year: *The Outsider* by Colin Wilson (Gollancz) in which an earnest young man imparts his discovery to the world that genius is prone to *Weltschmerz*.

1957   As a memento, *The Hungarian Revolution*, edited by Melvin Lasky (Secker & Warburg) is the most effective document on those ten black November days which shook the world. The text and photographs still seem to echo that last terrible broadcast cry of the Hungarian Writers' Federation for 'Help! Help! Help!', which found no answer.

But an indirect answer is Professor K. R. Popper's *The Poverty of Historicism* (Routledge and Kegan Paul)—a deadly exposure of the 'law-makers' of History from Hegel via Marx to Spengler and Toynbee. It is probably the only book published this year which will outlive this century.

Why is Rumer Godden treated as a kind of Cinderella and hardly ever mentioned in essays on contemporary literature? *The Lady and the Unicorn* (Peter Davies) and her earlier *Black Narcissus* are perhaps the only novels on India that bear comparison with *A Passage to India*; I always thought of her as a kind of feminine incarnation of E. M. Forster.

1958 Missed year.

1959 William Golding's *Free Fall* strikes me as the noblest failure of the year. Oddly enough, it contains a quite unintentional summing up of the most ambiguous success of the year: 'He [an ageing, mad parson] was incapable of approaching a child straight because of the ingrown and festering desires that poisoned him. He must have had pictures of lucid and blameless academes where youth and experience could walk and make love. But the thing itself in this vineless and unolived landscape was nothing but furtive dirt.'

By which, of course, I do not mean to say that *Lolita* (Weidenfeld and Nicolson) is dirt; she has, rather the fascination of a lollipop flavoured with sulphuric acid.

Lastly, Gertrude Himmelfarb's *Darwin and the Darwinian Revolution* (Chatto)—the most valuable contribution to the Centenary.

1960 While I read Constantine Fitz Gibbon's *When the Kissing Had to Stop* (Cassell) I felt as, I imagine, a patient feels during electric-convulsion therapy: but therapy it is and it should be made obligatory reading for all Aldermaston marchers in their wigwams around the camp fires. Equally therapeutic in effect, but gentler in method, is Mary Benson's biography of *Tshekedi Khama* (Faber), a rare blend of scholarly precision and feminine intuition. Lastly, Professor R. O. Kapp's *Towards a Unified Cosmology* (Hutchinson) is, pending observational verification, the most stimulating cosmological speculation since the Hoyle–Bondi–Gold hypothesis of continuous creation.

1961 One should never underrate the enemy's strength: I am sorry to confess that my choices this year were all written by women. I found Zoë Oldenbourg's *Massacre at Montségur*: A History of the Albigensian Crusade (Weidenfeld and Nicolson) the year's most fascinating work on History; Mary B. Hesse's *Forces and Fields* (Nelson) the most important work on the History of Science; and *Clock Without Hands*, by Carson McCullers (Cresset), the best novel.

1962 L. L. Whyte's *The Unconscious Before Freud* (Tavistock Publications) has more to offer than the title promises. It not only traces the ancestry of Freud back to antiquity, but puts the whole problem of consciousness into a new perspective.

Cyril Connolly is the founder of a philosophy which future historians might call Dialectical Hedonism (*Angst durch Freude*). His latest exercise in nostalgia, *Les Pavillons* (Hamish Hamilton), is all the more enjoyable as it shows a reassuring improvement of the Pleasure to Angst ratio.

Michael Davidson's autobiography, *The World, The Flesh and Myself* (Arthur Barker), starts with the sentence: 'This is the life-history of a lover of boys.' It is, in fact, the two-fold story of a courageous and lovable person's struggle to come to terms with his Grecian heresy and of a brilliant journalist's fight against colonial jingoism from Zululand to Cyprus.

1963 Dr. Gombrich's latest work, *Meditations on a Hobby Horse* (Phaidon Press), again combines scientific precision with intuition, art criticism with a solid mastery of psychology; his hobby horse has wings.

Inventing the Future, by Professor Dennis Gabor (Secker and Warburg), is a compressed but comprehensive account of the great crisis man has to face during the next few decades, and of the means to overcome it—original, non-Utopian, but soberly (and enviably) optimistic.

Among the novels, I liked and disliked best Mary McCarthy's *The Group* (Weidenfeld and Nicolson) for her vitriolic compassion towards her sex and generation.

1964 For the fourth time a novel by William Golding heads

196

my list in this annual game. It is fascinating to watch how he keeps attempting the seemingly impossible, using the medium of the conventional novel to do things which transcend its scope. In *The Inheritors* his characters were Neanderthal men of the last Ice Age; in *Pincher Martin* the whole action consisted in the fantasies of a drowning man and took place in a few seconds; his last book, *The Spire* (Faber), could be called a mystery play on constructional engineering. Each of them is a *tour de force*, but the forcing is done with the delicate touch of a surgeon or poet.

In *Life with Picasso*, Françoise Gilot (in collaboration with Carlton Lake; to be published by Nelson) has painted a portrait of a genius which is a masterpiece in its own right; I cannot recall any book of the 'Life with' genre equally vivid, penetrating, merciless and forgiving.

Paperback choice: *Man on his Nature*, by Sir Charles Sherrington (Cambridge). Written more than twenty-five years ago, this grand synthesis has remained astonishingly fresh and rewarding.

1965 Sir Alister Hardy's *The Living Stream* (Collins) has the provocative sub-title: 'A Restatement of Evolution Theory and its Relation to the Spirit of Man.' Based on the author's Gifford Lectures, it is a challenge to the prevailing neo-Darwinian orthodoxy, and might signify a turning-point in the theory of evolution.

Paperback of the year: Joan Henry's novel, *Yield to the Night* (Panther), the story of a woman awaiting her execution. It has a haunting simplicity—and a paradoxically lyrical touch.

Lastly, *Love and Marriage* (Hart-Davis), by those two eight-year-old experts in the field, Daisy and Angela Ashford, reprinted for the first time, it seems, since 1920. ('They had for tea some cold ham, some toasted buns, a sago pudding, a dried bloater and a couple of shrimps.')

1966 I cannot think of any book I have read this year which

I am likely to want to read again in ten years' time. This also applies to A. E. Hotchner's *Papa Hemingway* (Weidenfeld and Nicolson); yet I feel that it will be quoted and commented on for a much longer period. Not for its literary qualities, which are indifferent, but for its documentary value: conveying artlessly but with a shattering impact the tragedy of a genius who created a new era in the art of writing.

1967 To anybody seriously interested in the problem of telepathy and kindred phenomena I recommend *Science and ESP*, edited by J. R. Smythies (Routledge), with a galaxy of contributors, including Sir Cyril Burt, Sir Alister Hardy, Professors C. D. Broad, H. H. Price and H. Morgenau.

Michael Meyer, to whom we owe the 'definitive' translations of fifteen of Ibsen's plays, has now written the first biography of the master to appear in forty years. The first of two volumes, *Henrik Ibsen—The Making of a Dramatist* (Hart-Davis) is a contribution of permanent value for students of the European theatre.

Among the few novels which I was able to read to the end, *Killing Time* (Dial Press, New York) by Thomas Berger stands out as an original and powerful tale of a saintly murderer.

The Horse in the Locomotive

Return Trip to Nirvana*

A few weeks ago I received a letter dated from Divinity Avenue, Cambridge, Massachusetts. That symbolic address refers to the Center for Research in Personality of Harvard University. The writer was a friend, an American psychiatrist working in that Department.†

Dear K . . .,

Things are happening here which I think will interest you. The big, new, hot issue these days in many American circles is DRUGS. Have you been tuned in on the noise?

I stumbled on the scene in the most holy manner. Spent last summer in Mexico. Anthropologist friend arrived one weekend with a bag of mushrooms bought from a witch. Magic mushrooms. I had never heard of them, but being a good host joined the crowd who ate them. Wow! Learned more in six hours than in past sixteen years. Visual transformations. Gone the perceptual machinery which clutters up our view of reality. Intuitive transformations. Gone the mental machinery which slices the world up into abstractions and concepts. Emotional

---

* First published in the *Sunday Telegraph*, 12.3.1961, with the editorial caption: 'Mystical Hallucinations induced by drugs are arousing controversy in America. After taking a mushroom drug used in Mexico, the author challenges Aldous Huxley's defence of the cult.'

† The friend in question was Dr. Timothy Leary who, a few years later, was to attain world-wide notoriety as the leader of the LSD cult.

transformations. Gone the emotional machinery that causes us to load life with our own ambitions and petty desires.

Came back to U.S.A. and have spent last six months pursuing these matters. Working with Aldous Huxley, Alan Watts [noted authority on Zen Buddhism], Allen Ginsberg the poet. We believe that the synthetics of the cactus peyote (mescalin) and the mushrooms (psilocybin) offer possibilities for expanding consciousness, changing perceptions, removing abstractions.

For the person who is prepared, they provide a soul-wrenching mystical experience. Remember your enlightenments in the Franco prison? Very similar to what we are producing. We have had cases of housewives who have never heard of Zen, experiencing *satori* [mystic enlightenment] and describing it. . . .

We are offering the experience to distinguished creative people. Artists, poets, writers, scholars. We've learned a tremendous amount by listening to them. . . .

We are also trying to build this experience in a holy and serious way into university curricula. . . . If you are interested I'll send some mushrooms over to you. . . . I'd like to hear about your reaction. . . .

Shortly afterwards, I went to the States, to participate in a Symposium at the University of California Medical Center in San Francisco.* One of the main subjects of the Symposium was 'The Influence of Drugs on the Individual'. But this was not much of a coincidence, as, at the present moment, a surprising number of Americans, from Brass to Beat, seem to have, for different reasons, drugs on the brain: the Brass because they are worried about brain-washing and space-flight training; the Beat because drugs provide a rocket-powered escape from reality; the Organisation Men because tranquillisers are more effective than the homely aspirins and fruit salts of yore; the medical profession because some of the new drugs promise a revolution, by 'chemical surgery', in the treatment of mental disease; and the spiritually frustrated on all levels of society because drugs promise a kind of do-it-yourself approach to Salvation. Thus there is a confluence of motives, and an inflation in academic

* See p. 213 ff.

drug-research projects, financed on a lavish scale by Government agencies, universities and foundations.

On the way from San Francisco to my friend at Harvard, I stayed for a few days at the University of Michigan at Ann Arbor. I had been invited there for quite different reasons, but on the first morning of my stay the subject of the magic mushroom cropped up. The psychiatrist in charge of the mushroom was an Englishman of the quiet, gentle, un-American kind. Based on his own experiences—he had taken it on several occasions—and on experiments with ten test-subjects, he ventured the tentative opinion that, compared to the fashionable wonder-drugs mescalin and lysergic acid, the effect of the mushroom was relatively harmless and entirely on the pleasant, euphoric side.

It is well known that the mental attitude, the mood in which one enters the gates of mushroomland, plays a decisive part in determining the nature of the experience. Since Dr. P. was such a pleasant person and the atmosphere of his clinic appealed to me, I volunteered as a guinea pig—though I felt a little guilty towards my enthusiastic friend in Harvard. We fixed the date of the experiment, and I was told not to make any appointments on that day until the evening, as I would remain under the influence of the drug for about six hours.

Just before awakening on the morning of the appointed day, I had a dream which is relevant to what follows. I saw standing before me a large earthenware jar; in it squatted a man, with only his head visible over the rim of the jar; the colour of his face was a yellowish brown, he seemed in great pain, but had a resigned look; a dispassionate voice explained to me that this was St. Michael undergoing martyrdom; and that presently he was to be lifted out and put into another jar to be boiled alive in oil. I woke up with a faint nausea, and at once connected the dream with an experience on the previous day. In one of the laboratories for experimental psychology, I had seen a monkey's head—its body was hidden behind an enclosure so that the head alone was visible. An electric plug had been inserted into the creature's skull, and a wire led from it to the ceiling. The plugged head was perfectly, unnaturally still (the body was immobilised in a restraining jacket); only the eyes, old as Methuselah's, turned in their sockets to follow the visitors' movements, quietly, resignedly.

I hasten to reassure the reader that, as far as human knowledge goes, the monkeys in these experiments do not suffer pain. The plug is connected to electrodes which are inserted into the brain under anaesthesia, and once placed, cause neither pain nor discomfort: the purpose of the experiment does not concern us here. I had read about it before; nevertheless, the sight of that sad little head, with the electric plug sticking out of its fur, filled me with an unreasoning horror; hence the dream about St. Michael's martyrdom. Thus I faced the mushrooms in a depressed state of 'floating anxiety', as the psychiatrists say.

The mushroom comes synthesised, in the shape of little pink pills; they look harmless and taste bitter. I swallowed nine of them (18 milligrams of psilocybin), which is a fair-sized dose for a person of my weight. They were supposed to start acting after thirty minutes, and reach their maximum effect after about an hour.

However, for nearly an hour nothing at all happened. I was chatting with Dr. P. and one of his assistants, first in his office, then in a room which had a comfortable couch in it and a tape recorder; after a while I was left alone in the room, but Dr. P. looked in from time to time. I lay down on the couch, and soon began to experience the kind of phenomena which have been repeatedly described by people who experimented with mescalin. When I closed my eyes I saw luminous, moving patterns of great beauty, which was highly enjoyable; then the patterns changed into planaria—a kind of flatworm which I had watched under the microscope the previous day in another laboratory; but the worms had a tendency to change into dragons, which was less enjoyable, so I walked out of the show simply by opening my eyes. Then I tried it again, this time directing the beam of the table-lamp, which had a strong bulb, straight at my closed eyelids, and the effect was quite spectacular—rather like the explosive paintings of schizophrenics, or Walt Disney's *Fantasia*. A flaming eddy, the funnel of a tornado, appeared over my head, drawing me upward; with a little auto-suggestion and self-dramatisation I could have called it a vision of myself as the prophet Elijah being taken to Heaven by a whirlwind. But I felt that this was buying one's visions on the cheap ('Carter's little mushrooms are the best, mystic experience guaranteed or money refunded'); so I again walked out of the show by forcing my eyes to open. It was as simple as that, and I congratulated myself on my sober self-control, a rational mind not to be fooled by little pills.

By now, however, even with open eyes, the room looked different. The colours had become not only more luminous and brilliant, but different in quality from any colour previously seen; they were located outside the normally visible spectrum, and to refer to them one would have to invent new words—so I shall say that the walls were breen, the curtains were darsh, and the sky outside emerdine. Also, one of the walls had acquired a concave bend like the inside of a barrel, the plaster statue of the Venus of Milo had acquired a grin, and the straight dado-line was now curved, which struck me as an exceedingly clever joke. But all this was quite unlike the wobbling world of drunkenness, for the transformed room was plunged into an underwater silence, where the faint hum of the tape recorder became obtrusively loud, and the almost imperceptible undulations of the curtains became the Ballet of the Flowing Folds (the undulations were caused by warm air ascending from the central-heating body). A narrow strip of the revolving spool of the tape recorder caught the gleam of the lamp every few seconds; this faint, intermittent spark, unnoticed before, observed out of the corner of the eye on the visual periphery became the revolving beam of a miniature lighthouse. This lowering of the sensory threshold and simultaneous heightening of the intensity and emotional significance of perceptions is one of the basic phenomena of the mushroom universe. The intermittent light-signal from the slowly revolving spool became important, meaningful and mysterious; it had some secret message. Afterwards I remembered, with sympathetic understanding, the fantasies of paranoiacs about hidden electric machines planted by their enemies to produce evil Rays and Influences.

The signalling tape recorder was the first symptom of a chemically induced state of insanity. The full effect came on with insidious smoothness and suddenness. Dr. P. came into the room, and a minute or two later I saw the light—and realised what a fool I had been to let myself be trapped by his cunning machinations. For during that minute or two he had undergone an unbelievable transformation.

It started with the colour of his face, which had become a sickly yellowish brown—the colour of the monkey with the electric plug. He stood in a corner of the room with his back to the green wall, and as I stared at him his face split into two, like a cell dividing. It oscillated for a while, then reunited into a single face, and by this time the transformation was complete. A small scar on the Doctor's neck, which I had not noticed before, was gaping wide, trying to ingest the flesh of the chin; one ear had shrunk, the other had grown by several inches, and the face became a smirking, evil phantasm. Then it changed again, into a different kind of Hogarthian vision, and these transformations went on for what I took to be several minutes.

All this time the doctor's body remained unchanged, the hallucinations were confined to the space from the neck upward; and they were strongly two-dimensional, like faces cut out of cardboard. The phenomenon was always strongest in that corner of the room where it had first occurred, and faded into less offensive distorting-mirror effects when we moved elsewhere, although the lighting of the room was uniform. The same happened when other members of the staff joined us later. One of them, the jovial Dr. F., was transformed into a vision so terrifying—a Mongol with a broken neck hanging from an invisible gallows—that I thought I was going to be sick; yet I could not stop myself staring at him. We stood face to face in the 'evil corner', and with my pupils dilated by the drug I must have looked unpleasant, for he asked in an embarrassed voice: 'Why are you staring at me so?' In the end I said: 'For God's sake let's snap out of it', and we moved into another part of the room, where the effect became much weaker.

As the last remark indicates, I was still in control of my outward behaviour, and this remained true throughout the whole three or four hours of the experience. But at the same time I had completely lost control over my perception of the world. I made repeated efforts 'to walk out of the show' as I had been able to do during the first stages on the couch, but I was powerless against the delusions. I kept repeating to myself: 'But these are nice, friendly people, they are your friends', and so on. It had no effect whatsoever on the spontaneous and inexorable visual transformations. At one stage, these spread from the faces of others to my own right hand which shrivelled into a cripple's, and to the metal bars of the table lamp, which were transformed into the claws of a predatory bird. Then I asked for a mirror to be brought in, expecting to see a picture of Dorian Gray. Strangely enough, there was no change in my own face.

After an hour or two (one's inner clock goes completely haywire under the drug), the effect began to wear off. They gave me a sedative, and after a suitable interval took me back to the hotel, where I had a meal with one of the doctors in the public dining-room. The world was normal again, except for a minute or two when the doctor's head, for the last time, went through two or three rapid mutations across the dining-table. These, however, were no longer frightening, but rather like a brilliant actor's impersonations of various character-types in quick succession—all of which, I felt with deep conviction, were different aspects of the doctor's personality. This conviction of possessing the gift of second sight, of being able not only to 'read' but to *see* a person's hidden character as if it were projected on a screen, is another typical symptom in certain forms of schizophrenia. I had faint recurrent whiffs of it for quite a while. The faces of friends or of strangers in the train would for a moment become unreal, like projections of a magic lantern, and at the same time revealing their innermost secret—but I never managed to express or define just what had been revealed. This was the only after-effect of the experience that I am aware of. It lasted for about a week.

When the mind is split into separate layers, some of which function more or less normally, while others are deranged, one exists in a world of paradoxa. At certain moments I thought that I had been lured into a trap, that the malign faces surrounding me were somehow connected with the Gestapo or the G.P.U., and it was a comfort to know that the room was on the first floor so that if it came to the worst I could bolt through the window. I always managed to snap out of it after a moment or two, persuading myself that all this was a delusion; but the *visual* delusions persisted independently of my better knowledge, and against these I was helpless. The horror of the experience lies not so much in the apparitions themselves, but in the moments of panicky suspicion that the condition might become irreversible.

And that suspicion is not entirely unfounded. One member of a medical research team whom I met, inadvertently took an overdose of the pills with the result that he suffered from intermittent delusions of persecution for a period of two months. I know of two other people who experimented under insufficient medical supervision and had to be hospitalised for varying periods. These, however, are exceptions. I have mentioned before that all of Dr. P.'s previous subjects had positive, euphoric experiences; I 'broke the series', as he ruefully remarked over post-mortem drinks on the next day. The same is true of the majority of the Harvard team's subjects. The reasons why I had been so unlucky are related to the monkey and the subsequent dream; they were the wrong kind of preparation. If one adds to this the burden of past experiences as a political prisoner, of past preoccupations with brain-washing, torture and the extraction of confessions, it will seem evident that I was a rather unfortunate choice for a guinea pig—except perhaps to demonstrate what mushroomland *can* do to the wrong kind of guinea pig. The phantom faces were equally obvious projections of a deep-seated resentment against being 'trapped' in a situation which carried symbolic echoes of the relation between prisoner and inquisitor, monkey and experimenter, persecutor and victim. Poor Dr. P. and his nice colleagues had to endure what they would call a 'negative transference', and serve as projection screens for the lantern slides of the past, stored in the mental underground. I suspect that a sizeable minority of people who try for a chemical lift to Heaven, will find themselves landed in the other place. This may be due to character or accident—the wrong time or setting for the experiment bringing the wrong type of lantern slides out of storage; and no experimental psychiatrist, however skilled, can exercise complete control over all the variables in the situation, nor guarantee the result.

I do not want to exaggerate the small risks involved in properly supervised experiments for legitimate research purposes; and I also believe that every clinical psychiatrist could derive immense benefits from a few experiments in chemically induced temporary psychosis, enabling him to see life through his patients' eyes. But I disagree with the enthusiasts' belief that mescalin or psilocybin, even when taken under the most favourable conditions, will provide artists, writers or aspiring mystics with new insights, or revelations, of a transcendental nature.

I profoundly admire Aldous Huxley, both for his philosophy and uncompromising sincerity. But I disagree with his advocacy of 'the chemical opening of doors into the Other World', and with his belief that drugs can procure 'what Catholic theologians call a gratuitous grace'.* Chemically induced hallucinations, delusions and raptures may be frightening or wonderfully gratifying; in either case

* *The Doors of Perception*, London, 1954.

they are in the nature of confidence tricks played on one's
own nervous system.

I have before me a file, compiled by the Harvard research
team, containing the productions of various writers and
scholars while under the influence of one of the drugs, or
shortly afterwards. The first, by a well-known novelist,
starts:

> Mainly I felt like a floating Khan on a magic carpet with my
> interesting lieutenants and gods . . . some ancient feeling about
> old geheuls in the grass, and temples, exactly also like the sen-
> sations I got drunk on pulgue floating in the Xochimilco
> gardens. . . .

The second, by an aspiring writer, starts:

> Dear . . . Experiences with Psilocybin in me have been very
> tastey & eatable & when the effects come on, wham, I am in
> the middle of this ever grower larger and larger cosmos of
> vibrating hums of wishes & desires & mistroy plays as in
> Shaskerpiere, about to enter the stage & speack in the play.
> Somehow these pills make the soul more real. . . . (The spelling
> is a semi-conscious mannerism often induced by the drug.)

The third is the beginning of a poem, also by a well-known
writer, called *Lysergic Acid (God seen thru Imagination)*:

> It is a multiple million eyed monster/it is in all its elephants
> and selves/it hummeth in the electric typewriter/it is electricity
> connected to itself, if it hath wires/it is a vast Spiderweb/and I
> am on the last millionth infinite tentacle of the spiderweb. . . .

Some of the reports in the file, written after the experience,
are in a more sober vein, but not a single item contains anything of artistic merit or of theoretical value; and the drug-
induced productions were all far beneath the writers' normal
standards (Huxley's report was not in the file). While working on the material I was reminded of a story George Orwell
once told me (I do not recall whether he published it): a
friend of his, while living in the Far East, smoked several
pipes of opium every night, and every night a single phrase

rang in his ear, which contained the whole secret of the universe; but in his euphoria he could not be bothered to write it down and by the morning it was gone. One night he managed to jot down the magic phrase after all, and in the morning he read: 'The banana is big, but its skin is even bigger.'

I had a similar revelation when I took the mushroom the second time, under more happy and relaxed conditions. This was in the apartment of my Harvard friend from whose letter I have quoted, and there were six of us in a convivial atmosphere, after dinner and wine. All of us took various amounts of the pill, and this time I took a little more (either 22 or 24 m/m, for I lost count). Again there were delusions: the room expanded and contracted in the most extraordinary manner, like an accordion played slowly; but the faces around me changed only slightly and in a pleasant manner, becoming more beautiful. Then came the Moment of Truth: a piece of chamber music played on a tape recorder. I had never heard music played like that before, I suddenly *understood* the very essence of music, the secret of its magic; the harmony of the spheres was revealed to me . . . Unfortunately, I was unable to tell the next day whether it had been a symphony or a quintet or a trio, and whether by Mendelssohn or Bach. I may just as well have listened to Liberace. It had nothing to do with genuine appreciation of music; my soul was steeped in cosmic schmalz. I sobered up, though, when a fellow mushroom-eater—an American writer whom I otherwise rather liked—began to declaim about Cosmic Awareness, Expanding Consciousness, Zen Enlightenment, and so forth. This struck me as downright obscene, more so than four-letter words. This pressure-cooker mysticism seemed the ultimate profanation. But my exaggerated reaction was no doubt also mushroom-conditioned, so I went to bed.

In *Heaven and Hell*, defending the mescalin ecstasy against the reproach of artificiality, Huxley, the most highly respected exponent of the cult, argues that 'in one way or another, all our experiences are chemically conditioned'; and that the great mystics of the past also 'worked systematically to modify their body chemistry . . . starving themselves into low blood sugar and a vitamin deficiency. They sang inter- minable psalms, thus increasing the amount of carbon dioxide in the lungs and the bloodstream, or, if they were orientals, they did breathing exercises to accomplish the same purpose.' There is, of course, a certain amount of truth in this on a purely physiological level, but the conclusions which Huxley draws, and the advice he tenders to modern man in search of a soul, are all the more distressing: 'Know- ing as he does . . . what are the chemical conditions of transcendental experience, the aspiring mystic should turn for technical help to the specialists in pharmacology, in bio-chemistry, in physiology and neurology . . .'

I would like to answer this with a parable. In the beloved Austrian mountains of my school-days, it took us about five to six hours to climb a 7,000-ft. peak. Today, many of them can be reached in a few minutes by cable-car, or ski-lift, or even by motorcar. Yet you still see thousands of schoolboys, middle-aged couples and elderly men puffing and panting up the steep path, groaning under the load of their knap- sacks. When they arrive at the alpine refuge near the summit, streaming with sweat, they shout for their traditional reward —a glass of shnapps and a plate of hot pea-soup. And then they look at the view—and then there is only a man and a mountain and a sky.

My point is not the virtue of sweat and toil. My point is that, although the view is the same, their vision is different from those who arrive by motorcar.

The Poverty of Psychology*

1   Pavlov in retreat

An age is drawing to its close in the history of psychology: the age of the dehumanisation of man. Words like 'purpose', 'volition', 'introspection', 'consciousness', 'insight', which used to be banned as obscene from the vocabulary of the so-called 'Behavioural Sciences', are triumphantly reasserting themselves—not as abstract philosophical concepts, but as indispensable descriptive tools, without which even a rat's actions in an experimental maze do not make sense. A minority of diehards still insist on treating Man as a conditioned-reflex automaton, and knowledge as the accretion of lucky random guesses. But they are the rearguard, heroically defending a lost cause—the Swiss Guard dying on the staircase of the Tuileries.

This state of affairs was vividly illustrated by a recent Symposium on 'Control of the Mind', organised by the University of California Medical Center in San Francisco. The participants, as usual on such occasions, were selected on the principle of Noah's Ark, i.e. that each species should be represented: they included neurophysiologists (Penfield and Hebb); psycho-pharmacologists (Kety, J. G. Miller and

* Abridged version of a series of three articles, originally published in *The Observer*, April–May 1961, under the title 'A New Look at the Mind'.

Cole); psychologists (Mace and A. Simon); a cytologist (Hydén) and so forth; but also, for good measure, one theologian (Father D'Arcy), and two Creative Writers (Aldous Huxley and myself. In American university parlance every Writer must be Creative; which may be the reason why so many take to the bottle). But for my inclusion in the list, I would have called it a distinguished gathering, and well suited for establishing Inter-Communicational Inter-Relationships (I still seem to suffer from over-exposure to academic verbal fallout).

The nicely ambiguous title was originally meant in the passive sense: 'control of the mind' not *over* this or that, but *by* this or that—more specifically, by drugs, brain-washing, mass propaganda, and the like. Yet by the end of the Symposium, the one consistent lesson that emerged was the astonishing control of the mind *over* the physical impact of drugs, brain-washings, and other forms of coercion.

The most outspoken statements on this basic issue came from Father D'Arcy, Penfield and Cole. That a Jesuit theologian should extol the powers of mind over matter was, of course, to be expected. One of the participants had half-seriously mentioned the possibility of Orwellian thought-control by drugs in the tap water; D'Arcy denied that such a possibility existed. 'There is a last, mysterious layer in the self that can never really be touched,' he amiably explained to the neurologists, 'an ultimate self which enables priests to withstand torture, madmen to retain a vestige of sanity, and brave soldiers to resist brain-washing.'

A surprising number of speakers arrived, in different terms and on different levels, at much the same conclusions; among them Wilder Penfield, one of the most distinguished neurologists alive. A few years ago, Penfield had revolution-ised the study of memory when he made his patients re-live scenes from their distant past by faint electric stimula-tion of the temporal lobes of their brains (exposed during a surgical operation). Thus Professor Penfield is certainly not the kind of philosophical idealist who would airily belittle the importance of brain mechanisms in the life of the mind. 'There is no evidence,' he stressed at the beginning of his paper, 'of any mental activity without some action of the brain.' Yet in his conclusions, and in subsequent panel discussions, he stated with equal emphasis his conviction that 'brain' and 'mind' are separate entities; and that, when it comes to the problem 'how the mind is attached to the body', we are no wiser today than Aristotle was when he asked that question 2,300 years ago. He had some scathing things to say about those contemporary Oxford philosophers who refuse to acknowledge the existence of a mind-body problem. He singled out Gilbert Ryle and A. J. Ayer, who some years ago had participated with Penfield in a famous B.B.C. Third Programme series on 'The Physical Basis of Mind'.* Paradoxically, those participants in the series whose lifework was concerned with the anatomy, physiology, pathology and surgery of the brain, and whom one would have expected to take a materialist view, all took the opposite attitude; whereas the Logicians, whom one would have expected to show some respect for the mind, showed none at all, and seemed hypnotised by neural pathways and electrical circuitry. Professor Ryle, one of the foremost exponents of the Linguistic Philosophy of Oxford, compared belief in Mind with the belief of illiterate peasants who, on seeing the first railway locomotive, thought there was a horse hidden inside it. Professor Ayer had been equally scornful:

'The picture we are given [by the neurologists] is that of messages travelling through the brain, reaching a mysterious entity called the mind, receiving orders from it, and then travelling on. But since the mind has no position in space— it is by definition not the sort of thing that can have position in space—it does not literally make sense to talk of physical signals reaching it.'

To this Penfield replied in San Francisco: 'The problem should be stated in another way . . . Electrical currents pass through certain circuits of the brain, and there is simul-

* *The Physical Basis of Mind*, ed. Peter Laslett (London, 1950).

taneous change and movement in the conscious shapes that constitute the mind of man . . . To declare that these two things are one does not make them so. But it does block the progress of research.' He went on to quote the late Sir Charles Sherrington: 'That our being should consist of *two* fundamental elements offers, I suppose, no greater inherent improbability than that it should rest on one only . . . We have to regard the relation of mind to brain as still not merely unsolved, but still devoid of a basis of its very beginning.'

This was an exercise in true humility; and so was Penfield's admission that when the surgeon manipulates the brain of his patient, he has no idea of the philosophical implications of what he is doing:

> When the neurosurgeon applies an electrode to the motor area of the patient's cerebral cortex causing the opposite hand to move, and when he asks the patient why he moved the hand, the response is: 'I didn't do it. You made me do it.' Without adopting psychiatric terms like the ego, it may be said that the patient thinks of himself as having an existence separate from his body.

> Once when I warned such a patient of my intention to stimulate the motor areas of the cortex, and challenged him to keep his hand from moving when the electrode should be applied, he seized it with the other hand and struggled to hold it still. Thus, one hand, under the control of the right hemisphere driven by an electrode, and the other hand, which he controlled through the left hemisphere, were caused to struggle against each other. Behind the 'brain action' of one hemisphere was the patient's mind. Behind the action of the other hemisphere was the electrode directed by the mind of the surgeon. At least that was what the patient thought instinctively. You will say that proves nothing, and I must agree that it proves only the direction of our current thinking . . .

The end of this memorable paper showed that the neurologists' position was closer to that of our Oxford Jesuit's than to the Oxford Logicians':

> There are, as you see, many demonstrable mechanisms [in the brain]. They work for the purposes of the mind automatic-

ally when called upon. But what agency is it that calls upon
these mechanisms, choosing one rather than another? Is it
another mechanism or is there in the mind something of
different essence?

. . . In conclusion, it must be said that there is as yet no
scientific proof that the brain can control the mind, nor fully
explain the mind. The assumptions of materialism have never
been substantiated. Science throws no light on the nature of the
spirit . . .

Not so long ago, the orthodox cohorts would have risen at
this from their chairs, waving their battle-axes and chanting
the Behaviourist Anthem:

> Hocus pocus spiritus—
> Stimulus responsibus—
> Holy Pavlov pray for us!
> Smite the heathen!
>   Block his synapses!
> Extinguish his reflexes!
> Put him into a Skinner box!
>   Get Hebb and Hull into his skull!
> Make him behave, behave, *behave!*

The third paper I mentioned earlier on was by Jonathan
Cole, Chief of the Psychopharmacology Department of the
National Institutes of Health. Its effect was that of a bucket
of cold water thrown at the drug enthusiasts of all persuasions
—from those who expect mystic revelations through mescalin, to those who treat man as a slot-machine with predictable responses to chemical stimuli:

To date, clinicians have been notably unsuccessful in pre-
dicting which patients will respond in which ways . . . There is
considerable evidence that the individual's expectations, the
atmosphere of the environment, and the attitudes of the therapist, may significantly alter the effectiveness of the drug. I am
beginning to have suspicions that the human setting may be as
important as, or more important than, the drugs . . .

The illustrations Cole gave were striking. In recent experiments, 120 college students were given a pill and then had to do a written performance test. One group were told that the pill was dexedrine, a well-known stimulant and energiser. Another group were told that they had been given a sleeping pill. In fact, however, *all* the students were given either dexedrine or placebos—dummy pills. The results of the test showed that the group who thought they had swallowed a pep-pill were full of pep, and the group who thought they had swallowed a sleeping pill became sluggish and sleepy.

Cole then turned to the hallucinogenic wonder-drugs mescalin, LSD and psilocybin, and described how the same drug—LSD, for instance—seems to produce one kind of effect on the sober East Coast and another in eccentric California. 'The subjects of Wapner and Kruse on the East Coast suffered some distortions in the visual field, but otherwise they never mention any subjective effect whatever ... Hartmann and his co-workers, on the other hand, working in Los Angeles, seemed to be able to induce most subjects to experience cosmic events such as union with the sun, or death and rebirth, with comparative ease.' Inevitably one is reminded of those patients under psycho-therapeutic treatment who will produce Freudian or Jungian dreams, custom-built to fit the analyst's requirements.

That suggestion and auto-suggestion play a considerable part in any form of therapy is not new; new is that this part is incomparably more important than the physicians, and even psychiatrists, of the age of reason ever dreamt. At a conservative estimate, about one-third of patients in any hospital ward are 'placebo-reactors' who will respond to dummy pills as if they were what they believe them to be.

But this unsuspected degree of suggestibility is not confined to hospital wards. Various universities are currently engaged in high-pressure research programmes on 'sensory deprivation' or 'stimulus starvation'. The subject is made to lie on a rubber mattress or to float in lukewarm water, with goggles of frosted glass over his eyes, with earphones that emit a steady hum, and shields over the hands that prevent perception by touch. The experiments are supposed to yield information about the way that astronauts will react under similar monotonous conditions, and are also relevant to the brain-washing of prisoners kept in dark isolation cells.

At first, the reactions seemed neat and predictable: after a few hours or even less, the subjects became confused and unable to concentrate; then followed delusions, hallucinations, sensations of de-personalisation, etc. This led some eminent neurologists to formulate a theory, according to which the human organism can only function normally if subjected to a continuous and incessant bombardment by external stimuli; if this is not maintained, hallucinations are substituted for it. Future historians will probably quote this as a classic example of Psychiatry in the Age of the Juke Box. Several researchers promptly identified 'sensory deprivation' as a form of schizophrenia. One of them drew the conclusion that schizophrenia should be treated by overstimulation, another that it should be treated by understimulation. Typical of the general approach to the problem was a passage in the paper of one of the participants in our Symposium—an eminent neurologist of somewhat rigid ideas: 'Let us take a young, vigorous, healthy male, a College student . . .' This vigorous male, we learned, was strapped on a mattress, blinded with goggles, deprived of his chewing gum, deafened by hissing earphones, and told that he was expected to go cuckoo. What happened? He went cuckoo.

For the last two thousand years or more, several million experimental subjects—monks, nuns and contemplatives of every persuasion all over the world—have practised various techniques of self-inflicted sensory deprivation, meditating in immobile postures, eyes closed, in silent isolation for hours on end—with entirely different results. In one of the panel discussions, this fact was pointed out to the author of the paper, but it made little impression; he preferred to stick to the 'young vigorous male'. Nobody will deny, of course, that an abnormal situation maintained for an excessive length of time will create abnormal reactions; but the measure of what is excessive may vary, according to the person, from a few hours to several days, and the reaction may vary from rage-tantrums to the Yogi's shamadi. Recent, as yet unpublished, experiments (by Pollard and Jackson at Michigan University, Ann Arbor) have shown that the spectacular symptoms displayed by test subjects in short-term deprivation experiments 'were primarily obtained by systematically influencing the subjects' previous knowledge of the expected experimental results'—that is to say, once more by suggestion and auto-suggestion. When the subjects knew beforehand that they were expected to have hallucinations, they obliged by having them; but failed to do so when, under precisely the same experimental conditions, they were misled into believing that the purpose of the experiment was to test a harmless new drug.

A last example will show the influence of subjective attitudes on the outcome of apparently objective experimental results in an unexpected field. Dr. Robert Rosenthal, a bright young Assistant Professor of Psychology, University of North Dakota, was engaged in the classic type of experiment of teaching rats to run a maze. He gave one group of his research workers rats which, he explained, were geniuses, specially bred from a stock of rats with an exceptionally high IQ. To a second group of researchers he gave what he explained were 'stupid rats'. In fact, all rats were of the same common-or-garden breed. The score sheets of the 'genius rats' showed unmistakably that they learned to run the maze much faster than the 'stupid rats'. The only explanation Rosenthal could offer was that the bias in the research workers' minds was somehow transmitted to the rats—just how this was done he confessed not to know. These, and other experiments* on similar lines moved the *New York Herald Tribune's* Science Editor, Ubell, to comment: 'The results throw a pall over the entire range of psychological tests as reported by the psychologists over the last fifty years.'

* See *Experimenter Effects in Behavioural Research* by R. Rosenthal (New York, 1966).

All these confluent trends in neurophysiology, neuro-pharmacology, experimental psychology and psychotherapy demonstrate that the concept of the 'human organism' as a bundle of conditioned reflexes is an abstraction—the reality is the individual, an elusive entity, with a blur of unpredictability at its core which determines the organisms's reactions to the stimuli that impinge on it.

In a brilliant technical paper on the biochemistry of brain processes, Professor Hydén of Goeteborg quoted Konrad Lorenz: 'If you design an experiment to demonstrate reflex activity, then the poor creature never gets an opportunity to show that it can do more than just display a reflex activity. Such experiments are expressly designed to confirm the hypothesis—which is the worst thing an experiment can do.'

Nearly a century ago, Charles Darwin, as if aware of the shape of things to come, mocked at the stimulus-responsibus type of psychology: 'I laid a small wager with a dozen young men that they would not sneeze if they took snuff, although they all declared that they invariably did so; accordingly they all took a pinch, but from wishing much to succeed, not one sneezed, though their eyes watered, and all, without exception, had to pay me the wager.'*

If you hit the subject with a sledge-hammer, or pump a massive dose of pheno-barbital into his veins, he will pass out, and that is about as far as behavioural predictability goes; if you merely tickle him under the chin, or give him a milder pill, his response will, broadly speaking, no longer depend on the stimulus, but on his 'state of mind'—the blur at the centre of the blueprint. The pill is a chemical compound, and physicians used to believe that the gesture of handing out the pill was irrelevant to its action. Now we are discovering that the gesture is at least as important as the pill; and that we all live in a kind of psycho-magnetic field, saturated with energies that interact on an unconscious level, vulnerable to voodoos and love-philtre placebos (it is no coincidence that the peyote cactus and the sacred mushroom

* *The Expression of the Emotions in Man and Animals* (1872).

of the Aztecs, mescalin and psilocybin, are so much in demand).

Thus on a higher turn of the spiral we are once more plunged into the magic world, but with a more sophisticated awareness of the hidden powers of the mind; and thereby hangs a new tale, the dawn of a new era in the study of the human psyche.

2 Behold the lowly worm*

One of the last Palinurian joys of civilised middle age is to sit in front of the log-fire, sip a glass of brandy, and read the 'Worm-Runner's Digest'. Its full title is: 'An Informal Journal of Comparative Psychology, Published Irregularly by the Planaria Research Group, Department of Psychology, the University of Michigan'.

The editor of this journal is Professor James V. McConnell, an austere young experimental psychologist who, like many a good man before him, developed a passion for flatworms. Their fascination derives from the fact that they are the lowest creatures on the evolutionary ladder with a brain of sorts and a true central nervous system, but are at the same time the highest on the ladder among those which reproduce by fission. They multiply both asexually and sexually. In summer, they are liable to drop their tails and grow a new one, while the dropped tail will grow a new head. They can be sliced into five or six segments, each of which will develop all the missing organs and grow into a complete individual, as good as new.

When fully grown, however (which means about half an inch in length) the delights of fission yield to those of mating. These are further enhanced by the fact that they are hermaphrodites; while young, they function as males, but after more mature reflection, as females, who lay eggs. In the

* See footnote on p. 213. Reprinted as Introduction to *The Worm Returns*, ed. J. V. McConnell (New York, 1965).

adult animal both sets of reproductive organs are present, and though the male organs mature first, the two phases may overlap. To complicate matters still further, I must mention that during the mating season the worms become cannibals, devouring everything alive that comes their way, including their own previously discarded tails which were in the process of growing a new head. Thus the *status quo ante* is re-established, by feedback as it were. The head itself, however, is rarely eaten, and never by its own tail (though technically this would be possible because the mouth of the creature is near the centre of its belly, and equipped with a retractable sucker). All of this goes to show that when the flatworms were created, evolution was in a rather confused state, as if trying to decide whether sex was really necessary for progress; and, if so, whether male and female should co-habit in the literal sense, that is, dwell in the same body—or be sorted out once and for all.

The latter idea won, for better or worse, but the Planaria were not informed of this and were left in confusion. As a result, we can tell neither whether the creature is male or female, nor whether the products of its asexual fission are its descendants or its *Doppelgängers*. This is an old philosophical teaser, but McConnell's experiments were designed to ask a new, crucial question: does the regenerated individual preserve a 'personal memory'? Is it capable of 'remembering' what happened to it before the fission—before the world split into two? Does the head which grew a new tail 'remember' more than the tail which grew a new head? The questions have to be hedged around by quotation marks, for we are moving in muddy semantic waters. But they must not be taken lightly, because it is in the makeshift brain of the flatworm that the history of the mind originates.

That Planaria are capable of learning, and have a memory, was known for a long time. The experimental procedure designed by Thompson and McConnell consists in putting the worm into a shallow plastic trough, half an inch in diameter, twelve inches long, filled with aquarium water.

When the worm (who is normally kept in a fingerbowl of its own) gets accustomed to its new environment, it starts moving from one end of the trough to the other with its peculiar, snail-like gliding motion. Under the microscope its smooth and svelte body, with its algae-green and brown specks, looks rather pretty, though the squinting eyes are somewhat humourless—they are light-sensitive, but have no lenses and no pattern vision. Training the creature consists in suddenly flashing the strong light of two 100-watt bulbs on it, followed by an electric shock. In the untrained animal the light causes no reaction whatsoever, whereas the shock causes a sharp to violent contraction of the body. After a number of repetitions, the worm learns that the light is a signal heralding the shock, and contracts when the light is switched on. It has acquired a conditioned reflex.

The next step was to train the animal, then cut it into halves, allow both halves to regenerate, and to find out *how much of its acquired learning each regenerated individual retained.*

Here a slight difficulty arose. A severed head or tail will usually regenerate into a complete individual within a fortnight. To make sure that all internal organs had a chance to develop properly, an additional fortnight was allowed before testing began. Now four weeks are a long time in the life of a worm, and it is to be expected that it will forget a considerable amount of what it has previously learned—even if not distracted by being cut into two and having to build the missing halves. A control group was therefore trained and then kept idle for a month, to see how much 'brushing up' the worms needed to regain their former proficiency. The result was as follows: on the average a group of worms needs a hundred and fifty 'lessons' of light-followed-by-shock until it learns to respond to light alone. After four weeks' rest, the same group will need a refresher course of forty lessons to react reliably. Thus the 'saving' in the number of required lessons due to retention was $150 - 40 = 110$; that is to say, over 70 per cent, which is not bad at all.

And now let's go from the normal to the sliced-up animal.

Each half, after regeneration had been completed, was given a refresher course by the same method as the uncut animals. The astonishing result was that the 'tails' showed as much retention as did the 'heads'; and that both 'heads' and 'tails' showed as much retention—that is, 70-odd per cent—as the uncut animals. Similar results were obtained by other researchers, who taught flatworms to find their way through a simple maze. Again retention by 'heads' and by 'tails' was the same.

How is this possible? How does the tail retain memories of learning? And when the tail builds a new brain, how does it build the memory into it?

Confronted by this puzzle, the worm-runners went one step further. They trained a 'head', H_1, after cutting off its tail, T_1; they let H_1 grow a new tail, T_2; cut it off and let it grow a new head, H_2. This creature, $H_2 + T_2$ had anatomically not a single organ or mature tissue in common with the original $H_1 + T_1$—and yet it had retained a significant amount of its learning. How was the information transmitted?

The latest experiments are even more surrealistic. I have mentioned that with the onset of sexual maturity, the worms become cannibals. In two experiments (as yet unpublished) McConnell chopped up trained animals and fed them to untrained ones. The results seem to indicate, pending confirmation, that the cannibals fed on trained animals learned quicker than the controls which were kept on a normal lowbrow diet.* In the jargon of communication engineering, information is always 'fed' into a computer or an organism; here the metaphor became flesh.

Since the flatworm's tail has as good a memory as the head, one might be tempted to believe that its brain plays only a subordinate part. But this is not so. The animal's brain, though primitive, is the centre of its nervous system in which

* Since this article was written, these experiments have been confirmed by several research teams, though others still regard them as controversial.

the sensory impulses from the eyes and auricles converge, and from which motor impulses are conducted in two symmetrical nerve strands and their branches to other parts of the body. Moreover, experiments by Ernhart indicate, rather surprisingly, that two-headed flatworms (produced by a simple surgical technique) learn quicker than others; while animals whose brain has been removed were shown (by Hovey) to be incapable of learning. Once, however, the animal has been trained, the tail alone is sufficient to retain the memory. One can only conclude that the brain is indispensable for the *acquisition* of learning, but not for its *retention*. This means that the memory of the animal cannot be located in its brain and nervous system alone; it must be represented by chemical changes in cells throughout the body. One of the leading American neurologists, Professor Ralph Gerrard, has suggested that in the head of the flatworm memory is retained by neuron circuitry, whereas in the rest of the body it is retained in the form of a chemical imprint. This, too, was confirmed by experiment: trained worms were cut into two and made to regenerate in a liquid which contained a chemical 'memory eraser'. The 'heads' were not affected by it; but the 'tails' forgot all they had learned.

Now this is the point where the scandal begins, and where the lowly worm acquires an unexpected significance for one of the basic controversial issues of our time. According to the orthodox theory of genetics upheld this side of the Iron Curtain, the progress of evolution from amoeba to man is entirely due to random mutations plus natural selection. The mutational alterations in the genes which determine heredity are said to be purely accidental, and natural selection is supposed to act as a kind of automatic sorting machine which perpetuates favourable mutations, and rejects the others. The negative implication of this theory is that no trace of what the parents have experienced and learned in a lifetime is inherited by the offspring. The hereditary mechanism is deaf and blind to the requirements of the evolutionary progress which it serves. The genes—atomic units of heredity—are kept in the germ cells in hermetic isolation, sealed off from the rest of the parent body, and are passed on unchanged from one generation to the next—except for those purely accidental mutations on the evolutionary roulette board. Generations come and go, but their struggles exert no influence whatever on the hereditary substance of the race. Whoever defends the opposite view—that there may be an 'inheritance of acquired characteristics' which would invest evolution with a purposeful aspect—is considered to be guilty of the Larmarckian heresy, and is academically non-U.

The gentle flatworm is not the first animal to cause a breach, so to speak, in the battlements of orthodoxy. During the last five years or so, evidence has been steadily accumulating which does not seem to fit into the orthodox frame; the Planaria are merely the latest and most dramatic arrivals on the scene. They establish beyond any reasonable doubt the inheritance of acquired learning in *asexual* reproduction. (Up to now the worms have refused to reproduce sexually in captivity.) However, even this should be a sufficient shock to the accepted views on the mechanism of heredity, for asexual reproduction is after all *reproduction*. An English scientific weekly recently paid grudging tribute to McConnell's team, but at the same time reproached them because 'in reporting these experiments to the American Psychological Association, the authors have unfortunately described the worms which regenerate from halves of other worms as a second generation . . .' [which might] 'suggest to the casual reader that here is evidence of the inheritance of acquired characters'.

And evidence indeed it is, semantic subterfuges apart. The Ann Arbor laboratory now has a whole tribe of Tigrina, all descended from a single individual. Whether one describes these animals at the fifth or sixth remove from the parent body as 'generations' or 'regenerations' does not alter the fact that all they have in common with that parent body is a biochemically inherited blueprint, transmitted by specialised 'regeneration cells'—the asexual equivalent of sperm and ova. These regeneration cells (also referred to as 'embryo cells' or 'formative cells') are scattered in the parenchyma, the loose meshwork between the Planaria's muscles and internal organs. When a worm is cut into two—or six—fragments, and each of these recreates all the complex organs of the whole individual, we are faced with a process similar to embryonic development. The regeneration cells which are responsible for this development must carry a chemical blueprint of the complete animal, as the germ cells do in sexual development (though the details of the chemical mechanism may differ considerably). The decisive fact is that these blueprints *include the traces of memories and learning acquired during the lifetime of the ancestral animal*; and that these acquired characters are built into the brain and nervous system of the new animal. The differences between sexual and asexual reproduction are many; but this basic fact is not altered by them.

Of special importance in this respect is the neat 'eraser' experiment that I mentioned. Here matters become technical and I must oversimplify a little. One of the two highly complicated 'blueprinting' substances which play a decisive part in the mechanism of heredity is ribonucleic acid, RNA. It can be broken up by another substance, RNASE. This was the substance used as a memory eraser. Worms which were made to regenerate in strong solutions of RNASE frequently grew into eyeless or headless monsters—proof that the 'eraser' interfered with the chemically coded hereditary potentials. Very weak solutions of RNASE, however, merely retarded the regenerative process without visible deleterious effects—except for erasing the chemically impressed memories of acquired learning. It was an elegant method of proving that these memories had been incorporated into the blueprint; as the most recent and tentative additions to it, they were the first to be erased.

The flatworm studies are relatively new, but they are now being duplicated and continued by researchers in several universities. The results which I have described will probably be modified and reinterpreted in various details, but the

228

basic fact of the transmission of acquired experience by asexual heredity is no longer open to doubt; whereas, as matters stand at present, its transmission by sexual heredity is passionately denied by orthodox science. This leads to the perversely paradoxical conclusion that the lower animals must have an incomparably *more* efficient evolutionary mechanism at their disposal than the higher ones. But if this were really the case, then the advantages of sexual reproduction—greater individual variety—would dwindle to such insignificance compared to the enormous disadvantage of blocking the inheritability of acquired learning that, through the process of natural selection, fissioning creatures would soon have got the upper hand over mating creatures, sex would have been dropped as a bad bargain, and we would all multiply by budding.

In an excellent survey of *Darwin's Forgotten Theories*, in the 'Worm-Runner's Digest', T. H. Morrill writes that the present 'overwhelming preference for environmental selection of hereditary accident' might be due to a bias inherent in our extravert 'and accident-prone culture, causing its members to seek such an irrational rationale in the universe'. He quotes the orthodox view, according to which heredity can only be changed by 'high temperatures and energetic radiations which intensify the molecular chaos' (Muller), and compares it to the ageing Darwin's views in the *Descent of Man*: 'The birth both of the species and of the individual are equally parts of that grand sequence of events, which our minds refuse to accept as the result of blind chance.' Confronted with the neo-Darwinist orthodoxy of our day, the old man would not fare better than that other revenant in Dostoyevsky's *Grand Inquisitor*. To return for a last time to the 'Worm-Runner's Digest': 'The later theories of Darwin are at base the last expression in Western science of those old, fond dreams of men—that in its largest aspect, beyond the misery, grime and cataclysms of earth, life is a "striving towards a goal, a far circuit and a sure coming home".'

3   *The pioneer beyond the pale**

'Dr. Rhine arrived at my doorstep in Cambridge, Massachusetts, one morning in June, 1926,' relates Professor William McDougall in his preface to Rhine's first book, *Extra Sensory Perception*. Young Dr. Joseph Banks Rhine and his wife, Dr. Louisa Rhine, both University lecturers in biology, had 'burnt their boats, given up their careers and come over to psychical research . . . They were working scientists without worldly resources other than their earnings. I was filled with admiration and misgivings. Their action seemed to me magnificently rash.'

Both the admiration and the misgivings were to be proved justified. A year after that morning in June, the Rhines were installed as Researchers in Parapsychology at Duke University, North Carolina, where McDougall was head of the Psychology Department. But it took another seven years before Rhine, by then an Associate Professor, was permitted to establish officially his 'Parapsychology Laboratory'. It was an event of great symbolic importance: research into the dubious subjects of telepathy and clairvoyance had for the first time been recognised as academically respectable.

Rhine and his collaborators introduced rigorous scientific methods into the investigation of these elusive phenomena. The popular image of the psychic investigator as an uncritical believer and willing prey to fraudulent media has become an anachronism. The new school in parapsychology, which Rhine inaugurated, has carried matters to the opposite extreme in its almost fanatical devotion to statistical method, mathematical analysis, mechanised controls. The card-guessing and dice-throwing experiments, repeated over millions of experimental runs with thousands of random experimental subjects—often whole classes of schoolboys who have no idea what the experiment is about; the increasingly elaborate machinery for mechanical card-shuffling,

* See footnote on p. 213.

dice-throwing, randomising, recording, and what-have-you, have turned the study of Extra Sensory Perception into an empirical science as sober, down-to-earth—and all too often as dreary—as teaching rats to run a maze, or slicing up generations of flatworms. Even the terminology coined by Rhine: ESP, Psi effect, decline effect, reinforcement, BM (blind matching), BT (basic theory), SO (stimulus object), STM (screen touch match), and so forth, is characteristic of the antiseptic atmosphere in modern ESP labs. This New Look in parapsychology is partly a reflection of the prevailing fashion in research in general, but there is also an element in it of bending over backward to disarm suspicions and to meet the sceptic on his own empirical-statistical ground.

On the whole this sober, functional approach proved effective. Not only several universities, but such conservative bodies as the Royal Society of Medicine, the American Philosophical Association, the Rockefeller, Fulbright and Ciba Foundations, have organised lectures and symposia on parapsychology. But the majority of academic psychologists remained hostile, although the giants had always taken telepathy and allied phenomena for granted—from Charcot and Richet through William James to Freud and Jung. Freud thought that telepathy entered into the relations between analyst and patient, and Jung has even coined a new name for an old phenomenon: Synchronicity. However, these men belonged to a mellower generation, and formed their conclusions before Rhine put parapsychology 'on the map'; among the younger lights, the attitude of H. J. Eysenck is significant. Professor Eysenck occupies the Chair in Psychology at the University of London, and is Director of the Psychological Department at the Maudsley and Bethlem Royal Hospitals. Those acquainted with his work will hardly accuse him of a lack of scepticism or an excess of humility. His summing up of the problem of telepathy commands some interest:

> Unless there is a gigantic conspiracy involving some thirty
> University departments all over the world, and several hundred

highly respected scientists in various fields, many of them originally hostile to the claims of the psychical researchers, the only
conclusion the unbiased observer can come to must be that
there does exist a small number of people who obtain knowledge existing either in other people's minds, or in the outer
world, by means as yet unknown to science. This should not be
interpreted as giving any support to such notions as survival
after death, philosophical idealism, or anything else . . .

In one sense, therefore, it can be said that Rhine's pioneer-
ing work has succeeded. But there is another side to the
picture; I became painfully aware of this during the three
days I spent at Duke. I liked this medium-sized, neat and
modern University, founded by a tobacco-growing million-
aire in the woodlands of Carolina; and I took an immediate
liking to both Rhines and their closest collaborator over the
last thirty years, Professor J. G. Pratt. Rhine's burly figure,
his broad, open face, his obvious sincerity, made me think of
a woodcutter, and indeed, his favourite hobby is to wander
into the woods with an axe and chop up a tree. Yet during
my whole stay I had a feeling that these admirable people
were living under a cloud, have become accustomed to its
shadow, and accept it as unavoidable.

If visitors from abroad come to Duke—and there is a
steady stream of them—they come for the sole purpose of
visiting the Parapsychology Laboratory, as pilgrims came to
Prado to hear Pablo Casals. Yet to the students in Duke,
Rhine's work is practically unknown, mainly, it seems, because their teachers discourage them from getting acquainted
with it. Members of other faculties still consider the parapsy-
chologists as beyond the academic pale. To say that the Rhines
are ostracised would be to put it too dramatically; but they
are lone figures in the landscape, and they are resigned to it.

They are equally resigned to the periodic storms of
defamation that break over their heads every two or three
years. The critics fall into two main categories: the first one
might call the 'insatiable perfectionists' who attack mainly
the earlier work on ESP when experimental controls were

not as rigorous as they are today; and the *a priorists*, who argue that ESP is a new and improbable hypothesis; that the hypothesis of fraud is easier to fit into the accepted framework of science; and that accordingly, by applying Occam's razor, one must accept the hypothesis of fraud. To this they usually add: 'No personal offence meant, we are merely engaged in an exercise in logic.' To quote Eysenck again:

> The very possibility of extra-sensory perception, or psycho-kinesis, appears contrary to modern scientific logic, and many people have shown considerable reluctance even to look at the evidence that has been produced in favour of these alleged abilities . . . Scientists, especially when they leave the particular field in which they have specialised, are just as ordinary, pig-headed, and unreasonable as anybody else, and their unusually high intelligence only makes their prejudices all the more dangerous . . .

*   *   *

I started the first of this series of articles with a remark to the effect that the age of de-humanised psychology was drawing to its close, and that the 'man-a-machine' school was fighting a rearguard action. Some friends have objected that I was too optimistic, but I do not think so.

No doubt the rearguard is still firmly entrenched in university chairs, the editorial offices of technical papers, and other positions of power. In the period of scholastic decline, the orthodox Aristotelians had occupied similar key positions. However, by clinging to a system of ideas which had been progressive in its time, and by carrying it to absurd extremes, the hollowness of its implied axioms was revealed, and orthodoxy hastened to its own doom. 'They are Folly's servants,' declared Erasmus, denouncing the sterile pedantry and grotesque academic jargon of his time. One wonders how he would react today to the definition of human beings as 'need-fulfilling, goal-achieving unities' (this comes from a book by a professor in the social sciences, called *Understanding Organisational Behaviour*); or to a book on nursery care in which the chapter on babies' tummy-aches is called 'Eliminatory Behaviour-Patterns'; or to statements by some eminent neurologists at a Symposium on 'Brain Mechanisms and Consciousness', such as: 'The existence of something called consciousness is a venerable *hypothesis*, not a datum, not directly observable'; or: 'Although we cannot get along without the concept of consciousness, actually there is no such thing.' My ears are still buzzing with similar statements in discussions at four different American universities. Nevertheless I believe that this era is drawing to its close, and that a new era is in the making in the study of the mind. Some of the new departures which I have mentioned, though still tentative and inconclusive if taken each by itself, seem to me symptomatic of the new trend.

Among the sure signs that some one-sided school of science has run into a dead-end are disillusionment and boredom. Orthodoxies are rarely felled by the stroke of a single genius. As a science editor in bygone days, I noticed that the favourite argument of cranks was to invoke the example of Galileo and the Inquisition. They never realise that the collapse of mediaeval philosophy was not brought about by Galileo's apocryphal *E pur si muove*, but by the fact that it had reduced itself to absurdity.

Something similar seems to be happening to the present orthodox view of the nature of man. The doctrines on which it rests, and which are beginning to reveal themselves as based on faulty axioms, can be summed up in a somewhat simplified form: that biological evolution is the outcome of random mutations preserved by natural selection; that mental evolution is the outcome of random tries preserved by 'reinforcements'; and that man is a self-regulating, passive automaton, whose actions consist in jerking out adaptive responses to stimuli in the environment.

'After all,' as somebody has said—I believe it was Freud—'after all, the most effective adaptation of the organism to its environment is to die.' Yet even the lowly worm, sliced into six pieces, knows better.

The Daemon of Socrates

Condensed version of a paper read at the Conference on
Brain Function and Learning of the Brain Research Institute,
University of California, Los Angeles. *

Creative activity could be described as a type of learning
process where teacher and pupil are located in the same
individual. Creative people like to ascribe the role of the
teacher to an entity they call the unconscious, which they
regard as a kind of Socratic demon—while others deny its
existence, and still others are prepared to admit it but deplore
the ambiguity of the concept. I belong to this last group; and
I believe that the ambiguity is mainly due to the venerable
tradition of applying the same word to a variety of different
phenomena.

The first of these phenomena is *awareness of an on-going*
activity. It is a trivial fact of experience that awareness is not
an all-or-nothing affair but a matter of degrees, a continuum
which extends from the unconsciousness that results from
being hit on the head, through the extra-consciousness of
visceral processes, through tying one's shoelaces with an
absent mind, through fringe-conscious perceptions and
routines, up to the laser-beam of focal consciousness. These

* First printed in the proceedings of the Conference published by the
UCLA Forum in Medical Sciences, 1967.

states can be arranged on a linear gradient—white through grey to black. Bright new skills acquired by learning— whether perceptual, motor or cognitive skills—tend to condensate into habits, and to migrate to the twilight zone. I can carry on a conversation while driving the car, and hand over control to the automatic pilot in my nervous system. Gastaut and Beck[1] have suggested that well-established habits may be handed down from the cortico-reticular level to the lymbic system or other structures in the diencephalon. But this mechanism seems a bit too crude to account for those fine shadings along the gradient. However that may be, let us note that *automatised skills do not necessarily become rigid and stereotyped*. Driving a car requires a flexible strategy; and the night-club pianist who transposes a tune into a different key or syncopates Chopin, while carrying on a flirtation with the barmaid, displays great virtuosity, although he functions semi-automatically, on the lower reaches of the gradient of awareness.

Thus habit-formation entails a constant downward traffic along that gradient, as on a moving escalator. But this downgrading does not necessarily involve an impoverishment of the skill, and does not exclude virtuosity of a kind which is often mistaken for creativity. Watch a locksmith at work as he feels his way with a simple bent wire in a complicated lock and snaps it open, as if guided by some mysterious intuition. In fact his performance is controlled by certain *fixed rules* of the game which apply to all locks in general, and a flexible *strategy*, both derived from countless past experiences, and sent down the escalator belt. The much-admired masters of the various Zen arts, from fencing to caligraphic painting, have always aimed at precisely this kind of virtuosity, confusing *unconscious automatisms with unconscious inspiration*. To ride a bicycle over a tightrope, or to perform the feats of a calculating prodigy, are admirable achievements, but at the opposite pole to creative originality.

So if we say that creativity relies, at certain critical moments, on inspirations of unconscious origin, we mean some kind of *upward* traffic on the escalator belt. This can be interpreted in more than one way. 'Inspiration' can be taken to mean a message received from '*the* unconscious' conceived as an autonomous agency—a separate compartment of the mind in which the Socratic demon does your homework for you. I believe this view to be untenable, although it was upheld not only by romantically inclined artists, but also by mathematicians like Poincaré. The very term 'the unconscious', used as a noun, is rather misleading because it implies a structural entity, a kind of box inside which certain activities take place, whereas in fact awareness is a variable *dimension* of activities. One and the same activity can be accompanied by varying degrees of awareness; even visceral functions can apparently be brought under conscious control by Yoga techniques or by Valsalva manoeuvring.[2] The opposite kind of thing happens when on awakening you try to hang on to the remembrance of a dream which is running away like quick-sand from conscious reach. One might call this phenomenon *oneirolysis*—from 'oneiros', dream, plus 'lysis', dissolution—I shall return to it in a moment.

If we discard the notion of 'the unconscious' acting as a *deus ex machina*, we can adopt an alternative, more sober interpretation. In this view the experience of sudden illumination, the apparently spontaneous creative leap appears as the result of mental events of a known and definable type, which, however, took place on the lower reaches of the gradient, below the level of focal or even peripheral awareness. The puzzling question is why these dark interludes are apparently indispensable to the wide-awake pursuits of science. The first, rough answer that suggests itself is that the particular type of mental activity which takes place in the so-called 'period of incubation' does not meet the criteria of articulateness and logical decency required for admission into the focal awareness of the wide-awake state—for the very good reason that if given unrestricted access, it would play havoc with our every-day thinking routines. But under exceptional circumstances, when routine breaks down, a temporary regression to these pre-rational forms of mentation often just does the trick.

Let me first discuss what *kind* of trick is wanted; and then how regression to pre-rational levels may help to perform it.

Original discoveries range from the highly dramatic to the deceptively simple; but there is a basic pattern underlying the whole range. It can be summed up in the single word, to cogitate, derived from *co-agitare*—to shake together what has previously been separate. Köhler's chimpanzees were skilled in grabbing bananas placed outside the cage by squeezing an arm or leg through the bars; call this skill No. 1. They had also acquired the habit of using sticks playfully to scrape the earth or push objects about; skill No. 2. When a banana is placed outside the chimpanzee's reach, it will for a long time persist in its hopeless attempts to reach it by applying the routines of skill No. 1—until the dramatic moment when its eyes focus on the stick lying about in the cage, grabs it and uses it as a rake—for the first time combining the two hitherto separate skills.

An impressive number of human discoveries is based on the same pattern: where some playful *l'art pour l'art* technique provides the unexpected solution to a problem in a quite different field. Galileo astonished the world when he turned a primitive toy invented by Dutch opticians into a tool for astronomers; the geometry of conic sections which Apollonius of Perga had studied in the fourth century B.C., just for the fun of it, provided Kepler, two thousand years later, with his elliptical orbits. The mathematics of probability originated in Pascal's interest in the Chevalier de Mèrè's passion for gambling; relativity and quantum mechanics owe almost everything to the non-Euclidian geometries and other absurd games played by mathematicians *seul en l'honneur de l'esprit humain*—as one of them said. The act of creation does not create something out of nothing; it reshuffles, combines, synthesises already existing facts, ideas, frames of reference, cognitive skills. Hebb's phase sequence hypothesis[3] led him to similar conclusions, based on physiological considerations. Perhaps Schmidt or Hyden will one day come up with a model of superimposed frequency-modulation patterns in neuron networks.

Newton combined Kepler's laws of planetary motion with Galileo's laws of the motion of projectiles; he put two and two together to make five. The more familiar the parts, the more striking the new whole. The motions of the tides and the phases of the moon had been separately known for time immemorial, but again it took a Newton to put them together. Gutenberg invented the printing-press with movable type by combining the techniques of the coin-stamp with the technique of the wine-press. Darwin hit on evolution by natural selection through combining zoological data with Malthus' essay on human populations. Maxwell borrowed from hydrodynamics to make a model for the propagation of electro-magnetic waves.

This act of cross-fertilisation—or rather self-fertilisation between two cognitive matrices in a single brain—seems to me the essence of the creative act; I have proposed for it the term 'bisociation' to distinguish it from the routines of associative thinking within the framework of a single matrix. The term 'matrix' is used here to refer to any ability, habit, or skill governed by a fixed code of 'rules of the game' which lends it coherence and stability, but leaves sufficient degrees of freedom for flexible strategies adapted to the environmental input. I have tried to show elsewhere that the concept of the matrix as a behavioural system with an invariant 'code' and variable strategies has a wide range of applicability on all levels of the organic hierarchy. However, today we are only concerned with *cognitive* matrices; i.e. with the cognitive structures that we variously call frames of reference, associative contexts, universes of discourse, mental sets, schemata, etc., including those vestigial forms of mentation which reflect an earlier phase in the development of the individual or of the species. (The nice ambiguity of the term 'code'—Highway Code, 'coded' message—reflects the

239

property of the nervous system to regulate bodily actions by means of coded signals.)

When life presents us with a problem, it will be attacked in accordance with the code of rules which enabled us to deal with similar problems in the past. When the same kind of task is repeatedly encountered in the same kind of setting, the responses will become stereotyped and degenerate into rigid patterns. *Vice versa*, a variable environment will tend to create flexible patterns. However, novelty can be carried to a point—by life or in the laboratory—where the situation still resembles in some aspects other situations encountered in the past, but contains new features, data, or complexities which make it impossible to solve the problem by the same rules of the game which were applied to those past situations. When this happens, the problem is blocked—though the subject may realise this fact only after a series of hopeless tries—or never at all.

A blocked situation increases the stress of the frustrated drive. When all promising attempts at solving the problem by traditional means—the period of 'conscious preparation'—have been exhausted, thinking tends to run in circles like cats in the puzzle-box, until the whole personality becomes saturated with the problem. At this stage—the 'period of incubation'—the single-mindedness of the creative obsession produces a state of receptivity, a readiness to pounce on favourable chance constellations and to profit from any casual hint. As Lloyd Morgan said: 'Saturate yourself through and through with your subject, and wait.' Thus in discoveries of the type in which both rational thinking and the trigger-action of chance play a noticeable part, the main contribution of unconscious activity is to keep the problem constantly on the agenda while conscious attention is occupied elsewhere—reading Malthus or watching the wine harvest. Our friend, the demon, seems to have bugged all primary cortical receptor areas with hidden microphones—to make sure that no bit of information of any conceivable use to him is lost.

Which is just another way of quoting Pasteur: 'Fortune favours only the prepared mind.'

But in other types of discovery unconscious mentation seems to intervene in more specific, active ways: first to encourage a promiscuous mixing of ideas, then to act as a matchmaker. Or, put it more respectably, it has a catabolic and an anabolic aspect.

The catabolic or regressive aspect is characterised by the relinquishing of certain rational controls which are necessary to maintain the disciplined routines of articulate thinking, but prevent the creative leap when routine is blocked. The result of this relaxing of controls is, metaphorically speaking, a kind of de-differentiation of the cognitive tissue, a regression from highly specialised, articulated levels of thinking to earlier, less disciplined forms of ideation, governed by more tolerant rules of the game. A frequent form of this is the retreat from precise verbal thinking to vague visual imagery. Jacques Hadamard's inquiry among American mathematicians[4] led to the striking conclusion that nearly all of them thought neither in verbal terms nor in precise algebraic symbols, but relied on visual imagery of a vague, hazy kind. Typical was Einstein's statement: 'The words of the language as they are written or spoken do not seem to play any role in my mechanism of thought . . . which relies on more or less clear images of a visual and some of a muscular type . . . It also seems to me that what you call full consciousness is a limit-case which can never be fully accomplished because consciousness is a narrow thing.' As far as one can gather from the record, the majority of scientists who have bothered to describe their working methods were visualisers, who seem to have shared Woodworth's opinion: 'Often we have to get away from speech in order to think clearly.' Watson was very naive indeed; and so are those among his successors who still equate thinking with 'implicit verbal behaviour'. Words crystallise thoughts, they give articulation and precision to vague images and hazy intuitions; but a crystal is no longer a liquid. Language can act as a screen between the thinker and reality; and creativity often starts where language ends, that is, by regressing to pre-verbal levels in the mental hierarchy.

More specifically this process of *reculer pour mieux sauter*—of a temporary regression preparing the forward leap—seems to trigger into action patterns of thinking that are prevalent in childhood and in primitive societies, but are normally under restraint in the civilised adult. Anthropology, psychiatry, and particularly the school of Piaget, have familiarised us with some common features of these otherwise very varied forms of mentation. Some of these features are: indifference to contradiction and to formal logic in general; the subjectivisation of space and time; regression from physical causality to magic causality and animism; the symbolisation, concretisation and dramatisation of abstract concepts; and a tendency to combine apparently incompatible ideas, to perceive hidden analogies between cabbages and kings.

The negative benefits of such regression are obvious. The code of rules which govern a routine performance, whether it is riding a bicycle or verbal reasoning, always operates on a lower level of awareness than the performance itself; the code is a hidden persuader. Lashley's dictum 'in all our perceptions we are aware of an organised structure; the organising is never experienced' seems to apply all along the way, from the visual constancy phenomena to the rules of grammar and syntax which operate in the gaps between words; to the prejudices and hidden axioms built into our reasoning routines. Regression implies a temporary suspension of these rules; the mind in labour is liberated from the tyranny of rigid, overprecise schemata; it is enabled to un-learn and acquire a new innocence of the eye, a greater fluidity of thought. (But of course also a greater gullibility; false inspirations, alas, carry the same spontaneous convincingness as the legitimate ones which they outnumber a thousandfold; the acid test of verification comes *after* the act.)

So much for the catabolic aspect; it dissolves the stubborn

embeddedness of ideas in their traditional context and enables us to perceive a familiar event from an unexpected angle, in a new light. But the unbedding of unsuitable partners in itself is not enough; the word 'intuition' implies some positive guidance toward more suitable ones. Alas, we have only indirect intimations of how that guidance works. I have just mentioned some features of those vestigial types of thinking; one of them was the *symbolisation* and *concretisation* of abstract concepts. This is precisely what Faraday did, who saw the magnetic 'lines of force' which he had invented as curves in space, and the whole universe patterned with these lines; and there is of course Kèkulé's hallucinated serpent. It reminds one of a painting by Blake; while the curves which crowd Faraday's universe recall the vortices in Van Gogh's skies. Then there is *magic causation*—which does not seem to be very helpful to a scientist. Yet Kepler founded modern astronomy on his belief that there is a 'virtue' or force emanating from the sun, which drives the planets as God the Father operates through the Holy Ghost. And when he first suggested that the tides are due to the attraction of the moon, Galileo, an eminently rational man, rightly rejected this as an occult fancy, a return to animism and magic. Newton adopted action-at-a-distance with the utmost reluctance (as his letter to Bentley shows)—and for the same reason. Post-Heisenberg physics is certainly not a regression to ancient magic; but the basic paradoxes of unpredictability, the relativisation of space and time—not to mention negative time and holes in space—are certainly easier to approach by that fluid type of thinking which permits one, like the Red Queen in Alice, to believe in six impossible things before breakfast. The recent prediction of the existence of the omega minus particle was prompted by a hunch strongly reminiscent of Pythagorean number-lore; so were some of Edington's speculations. Even more striking are the ever-recurrent assertions by physicists and mathematicians (Planck, Poincaré, Einstein, G. H. Hardy, Jacques Hadamard, and so on) epitomised in the laconic pronouncement of Dirac: 'It is more important to have beauty in one's equations than to have them fit experiment.'[5] Now beauty is one of the few things about which Cro-Magnon man knew as much as we do; and it seems that the road to the discovery of the positron led through the caves of Lascaux.

It has been said that the essence of discovery is to see an analogy where nobody had seen one before. And no doubt the most important kind of unconscious guidance is the unearthing of *hidden analogies*. But where was the analogy hidden and how is it found? Mathematics began, wrote Bertrand Russell, when it was discovered that a brace of pheasants and a couple of days have something in common: the number 2. An analogy of this kind is not hidden somewhere in a cupboard; it is created in the mind by abstracting a feature X which two phenomena have in common, although it is an inconspicuous feature further obscured by its embeddedness in two different contexts. It is not a logical procedure but a bisociative act. But once a new analogy has been created it is of course there for all to see—just as a poetic metaphor, once created, soon fades into a cliché.

Regression is apt to produce a rich harvest of wayward analogies. One example is the pun—analogy by sound—manifested in the dream, in slips of the tongue, and in the punning mania of children. Incidentally, Freud's emphasis on punning in the dream, which was regarded with some scepticism, has recently been vindicated by the experimental studies of Berger.[6] 'Its benefits to the poet are evident: the rhyme is merely a glorified pun, two strings of ideas bisociated in an acoustic knot. The same is true of what one might call optical puns: when Solomon compares the Shulamite's neck to a tower of ivory, he bisociates a visual form with two different meanings. There are a few discoveries on record which have apparently been inspired by such purely visual analogies (Harvey, Kelvin, Mitcherlich and the ubiquitous Kèkulé); but these dramatic cases are rather the exception.

Of much greater importance to our subject seems to me a form of unconscious guidance which is less direct. But it is also less easy to describe. The dream (or the drowsy day-dream) drifts effortlessly from one frame of reference to another, it bisociates in a passive, freewheeling manner. It churns out analogies which are useless (except for serving some intimate, private ends); which disintegrate when the dreamer awakes, and which he is unable to put into concise verbal shape—except by muttering, 'Something reminded me of something, but I don't know why.' This is what I called *oneirolysis*. Now in the throes of the creative obsession, when thinking on all levels is harnessed to the purpose, this process may perhaps be reversed into a kind of *oneirosynthesis*. This, of course, is only meant as a speculative pointer to the manner in which those 'somethings' vaguely reminding me of other 'somethings' condense into a nascent analogy. It may be a hazy, tentative affair, like Einstein's muscular sensations, and its shape may be changing from camel to weasel as Hamlet's cloud. The unconscious reaches of fertile minds must be teeming with such nascent analogies, hidden likenesses, and the cloudy forms of things unknown. But most clouds form and then dissolve again; and cloudbursts are a rarity.

To put it in another way: fifty years have passed since Ariens Kappers coined the term 'neurobiotaxis' for the growing towards each other of functionally related nerves until they make contact. In its original form the theory did not stand up to time; it was followed by a variety of others—chemical gradients, contact guidance, and so forth—to account for the puzzling mechanism which guides nerves to their functional destination. And there was Paul Weiss' remarkable salamander with its fifth transplantee leg which, within a short time, functioned in perfect synchronicity with the adjacent normal limb, although its muscles were supplied by nerve fibres which had split up in the scar at the place of grafting and whose branches had pressed forward until some of them had met the degenerated nerve-paths in the transplant's muscles in a completely randomised manner. When I first looked at the diagram of the branching, groping nerve-tree of the Weiss salamander, I was reminded of a famous passage in the *Logique de Port Royale* concerned with problem solving. It says, approximately, that if somebody wanted to discover whether he was a descendant of St. Louis, he could follow one of two methods, or a combination of both. He could trace St. Louis' descendants as they branch out downwards, or he could trace his own ancestors branching out and up; or start at both ends and see whether the branches meet. (The authors were equating the upward process with analysis, the downward with synthesis, but that formal distinction does not concern us.) Problem-solving can be described in terms of bridging the gap between the initial situation and the target by means of a mediating concept which will serve as a link. The search for it probably proceeds in much the same way as in the St. Louis case, by a fanning out of tentative hypotheses, groping in a vaguely sensed direction, guided by nascent analogies, following some unknown gradients or what-have-you. In other words, here opens a splendid vista of ignorance. All I mean is that when we hear repeated statements by mathematicians of the kind 'I have got my solution, but I don't know how I arrived at it' (Gauss), then we have no justification to reject out of hand the possibility of some such principle as envisaged, operating below the level of awareness—a kind of creative psychotaxis.*

* The remainder of this paper dealt with phenomena foreshadowing human creativity on lower rungs of the evolutionary ladder—a subject discussed at greater length in the last essay in this section.

REFERENCES

1. Gastaut, H. and Beck, E. 'Brain rhythms and learning.' *New Scientist*, March 1, 1962, **276,** 496–499.
2. Cf. e.g. McClure, Ch. M. In: *Calif. Medicine*, June 1959, Vol. 90, No. 6.

3. 'All our evidence thus points to the conclusion that a new insight consists of a re-combination of pre-existent mediating processes, not the sudden appearance of a wholly new process. Such re-combinations . . . we must consider . . . to be original and creative' (Hebb, D.O. *A Textbook of Psychology*, W. B. Saunders Co., London, 1958, 205).

4. Hadamard, J. *The Psychology of Invention in the Mathematical Field*. Princeton Univ. Press, Princeton, 1949.

5. Dirac, P. A. M. In: *Scientific American*, May 1963, Vol. 208, No. 5.

6. Berger, R. J. In: *Brit. J. Psychiat.*, 1963, **109**, 722.

Evolution and Revolution in the History of Science

Abridged text of opening address delivered to the General Science Section of the British Association Meeting at Cambridge, September 2, 1965.

I felt all the more honoured by the invitation to give this opening address as I am an outsider to the scientific establishment. On the other hand, the occasion seems to conform to the spirit of the times, where both cultures are busy putting up signposts with 'TRESPASSERS WELCOME—POACHING PERMITTED—ADMIRE OUR VIEWS—TELL US WHAT'S WRONG WITH THEM'. I intend to do just that.

I must start with some preliminary remarks on the psychology of creativity. By and large, one can distinguish between two extreme attitudes to this problem. One extreme is represented by that brand of Behaviourism which, for the last fifty years, from Thorndike through Watson and Hull to Professor Skinner of Harvard, had a dominant influence on American psychology. At the opposite extreme you have Gestalt psychologists, Jungians, existentialist psychologists, Zen Buddhists and Mescalin worshippers. The first relies on trial and error, and has an irritating likeness to our old friend, the monkey at the typewriter; the second relies on spontaneous intuitions, and reminds one of a medium in trance engaged in automatic writing. Which is closer to the truth?

When we look at a problem, we automatically start a search in our mental repertory for some rule or trick which has enabled us to solve similar problems. Routine problems can be recognised at a glance as analogous in some essential respect to other problems encountered in the past, which provides the appropriate technique to cope with them. But even routine problems require strategic skill in the selection and application of the correct sub-routines—such as extrapolation, intrapolation, schematisation, transformation of data. Above all, the more difficult type of routine task requires the *combination* of several sub-routines. Take the following cue from a crossword puzzle: '*Discussed a creature caught in the very act* (7 letters).' The act is 'deed'; the creature caught in it is a 'bat'—*de-bat-ed*—discussed. Next: '*Badly scare an Arab who was once a tough fighter* (7).' The Arab who was once a tough fighter is a *Saracen*, anagram of 'scare an'. Now solving a crossword does not require creative genius, not even an original mind. But it does require a flexible mind because the skill in question consists in fact of a hierarchy of sub-skills: the whole word or part of it could be an anagram; it could be a synonym; or a metaphor; or a play on words; or positional hint (the bat 'caught' in the centre of the deed); and there are several more sub-routines, each with its own rule of the game.

Now let me go back to my starting point and try to decide which of the two opposite views applies to crossword puzzle-solving: 'manipulation through trial and error' or 'spontaneous insight'. Trial and error there certainly is, but it is far from random because the range of the permissible tries is selectively limited by the rules of each game: synonyms, metaphor, positional shift, reversal of letters, etc. Even the anagram—which comes nearest to the monkey-at-the-typewriter situation—is not solved by random permutations, but by grouping letters into syllables, familiar prefixes and suffixes, and shifting, transforming, combining these subassemblies. The monkey is working on a hierarchically programmed typewriter which will only print sensible sequences. And as on each successive level of the hierarchy the rules of the game become more complex, the tries will become more sophisticated, the errors more refined. A long time ago, Bertrand Russell wrote that even a Newton could only learn to find his way through a maze by random tries. But some years later, it was discovered that even the rat, learning to run a new maze, proceeds by forming hypotheses. A hypothesis is an implicit try, and as we ascend to higher levels of the hierarchy the tries assume more and more implicit forms: tentative generalisations, empirical inductions, tentative combinations of ideas, lastly, guidance by hunches. The whole confusion in the psychology of problem-solving started with the fallacious identification of trial and error with randomness—with the behaviour of the angry cat in Thorndike's puzzle-box. But although to every research scientist the legitimacy of trial and error as an essential method of heuristics is obvious, the psychologist will only see it in its proper perspective if he stops thinking in terms of conditioned response chains, and starts thinking in terms of cognitive hierarchies.

This becomes at once more evident if we turn to the opposite view: that solutions appear by spontaneous insight, all in one piece, not by a process of elimination but of direct intuition, accompanied by that sudden emotional catharsis, the Eureka cry or *Aha* reaction. We all know those experiences of delicious euphoria following the solution of a quite trivial problem, when the bits suddenly fall into place, regardless whether the solution had been proceeded by fumbling trial and error or whether it came suddenly. For, in both cases, the essence of the matter is the emergence of order out of disorder, of signal out of noise, of harmony out of dissonance, of a meaningful whole out of meaningless bits, of cosmos out of chaos. This is the trigger which releases the cathartic reaction, whether occasioned by a mechanical puzzle falling into place or a new theorem being born.

But what, then, does 'spontaneous insight' mean? I think it means what I have just tried to say: the emergence of a new synthesis, of a whole on a higher level of the hierarchy than that of the parts which combined and fused into it. And the emergence of the new whole always gives the impression of spontaneity and suddenness regardless of how much fumbling preceded it, because the last decisive step in the combinatorial activity acts like a trigger on a Jack-in-the-box. Thus the strategy of solving routine problems consists in activating the appropriate sub-routines, in the appropriate order; but above all *in combining them in various ways when none of them alone leads to the solution.* This sounds trivial, but just this 'combinatorial activity' appears to be the key to creativeness.

So far I have only talked of routine problems; but where exactly do we draw the line between the solving of routine problems and creative originality? Let me quote two opinions—a historian's and a mathematician's. The historian, Thomas Kuhn, speaks of 'mopping-up-operations' which 'are what engage most scientists throughout their careers . . .' and mentions as the 'most striking feature' of normal research activities 'how little they aim to produce major novelties, conceptual or phenomenal'.[1] The mathematician, George Polya, defines a routine problem as one

> which can be solved either by substituting special data into a formerly solved general problem, or by following step by step, without any trace of originality, some well-worn, conspicuous example.[2]

He then contrasts these routines with the 'rules of discovery': 'the first rule of discovery is to have brains and good luck. The second rule of discovery is to sit tight and wait till you get a bright idea.' If one were to take this seriously, one would have to conclude that the cohorts of science consist exclusively of Generals and Privates, geniuses and handymen. Let us rather look at a concrete example and try to decide whether to call it a routine affair or an original discovery.

A couple of years ago, I read in a science column the following report about an electronics physicist in Albuquerque, New Mexico, who worked on radar equipment. His problem was to reduce the troublesome side-effects (of capacitance and inductance) in resistors, when brief pulses of high frequency currents are sent through them. One day, the article said,

> he let his mind wander and remembered an old parlour trick, the Möbius loop. Mathematics suddenly merged with electronics and he had what he was searching for.

A few months after this story appeared, you could see the new non-reactive 'Möbius resistor' advertised in the *Scientific American*. It is made by sticking two strips of aluminium tape to opposite sides of a non-conducting ribbon (made of plastic), then twisting it a half turn and joining the ends so that the conducting strips become a single loop, then soldering wire leads to opposite sides of the loop. If you now send an electric pulse through those leads, the current divides, flows in both directions through the foil and, since the Möbius loop has the perverse quality of possessing two sides, but only a single, continuous surface, the pulses apparently pass right through themselves. When the inventor was asked how exactly the thing worked, he replied: 'Maybe Maxwell could tell us, but he is dead.'

Now here you have a striking combinatorial achievement. Let us try to analyse the reasons why it is so striking. Three reasons come to mind. First, because it is an original combination which creates a novelty. In the second place, it is an unexpected combination because the two associative contexts which went into its making have previously each led a separate existence. In the third place, because the idea occurred to the inventor 'while he let his mind wander'; in other words, it came to him spontaneously without conscious effort. And since ideas must have an origin, we must conclude that it originated in some extra-conscious process.

Here, then, we have three factors: (*a*) originality; (*b*) the previous unrelatedness of the contexts which enter into the combination; we may, somewhat loosely, call this factor the improbability of the combination; and (*c*) the intervention of extra-conscious processes.

I have suggested in *The Act of Creation* that these three factors—plus a fourth to be added presently—may serve as criteria of what we call creativity. Let me briefly discuss each of them.

(*a*) Originality does not necessarily create novelty. Originality is a psychological concept, novelty a historical fact. There must have been many geniuses who left no mark on the annals of science, while others were conspicuous in priority disputes. According to a recent survey, multiple discoveries are not exceptions, but rather the rule in the history of science; thus Lord Kelvin's published papers contain at least thirty-two discoveries of his own which he subsequently found had also been made by others. The 'others' include men of genius such as Cavendish and Helmholtz, but also some lesser lights.

(*b*) 'Invention or discovery,' wrote Jacques Hadamard, 'be it in mathematics or anywhere else, takes place by combining ideas.'[3] In other words, it is the fusion or 'bisociation' of previously unconnected cognitive structures. Bisociation is a barbaric word, but it helps to focus attention on the specific character of the act; and about its importance there seems to be, for once, more or less general agreement among scientists and psychologists. To mention only a few, Poincaré in an oft-quoted lecture explained discovery as the result of a happy interlocking of the 'hooked atoms' of thought. According to Sir Frederick Bartlett, 'the most important feature of original experimental thinking is the discovery of overlap . . . where formerly only isolation and difference were recognised'. Jerome Bruner considers all forms of creativity a result of 'combinatorial activity'. McKellar talks of the 'fusion' of perceptions, Kubie of the 'discovery of unexpected connections between things', and so on back to Goethe's 'connect, always connect'. So far, then, we are on safe ground and we may feel encouraged to take a closer look at the bisociative process as a key to certain puzzling phenomena in the history of science.

We have seen that even solving a crossword involves combinatorial activities, often of a tricky kind—when, for instance, you have to employ riddle-solving techniques and anagram techniques at the same time. Why, then, not call this too a bisociative act? Because these various sub-routines are parts of a single, integrated skill of the experienced crossword-puzzler's, whereas Möbius loops and radar resistors belonged to separate contexts up to the moment when they suddenly fused in the inventor's mind. If the crossword-puzzler acquired his noble art untutored, and discovered all by himself that it requires the combination of two, or more, different techniques, then he would be entitled to call this a minor bisociation and even to shout Eureka. There is a hierarchic sequence of combinatorial processes in the development of the individual and in the historical development of science, resulting in a hierarchy of cognitive structures. The discoveries of yesterday are the commonplaces of today, and we marvel at mankind's erstwhile blindness in treating the motions of the moon and the motions of the tides as unrelated phenomena before they became inseparably fused in our minds. To recapitulate: although originality is a relative affair, each bisociative act, whether small or momentous, is a discrete step sharply set off from associative routine. Mental evolution is discontinuous, with quantum jumps, as it were, from one level of the hierarchy to the next.

This discontinuity is further reflected in the truism that the whole, the new synthesis, is more than the sum of its parts, and that its relational properties are to a large extent unpredictable by extrapolation from the properties of the parts. When Newton combined Kepler's laws of planetary motion with Galileo's studies of the motion of projectiles, a whole new universe sprang into being. One of the most dramatic chapters in the history of science is the series of mergers between previously separate disciplines, from Oersted's observation that the 'electric conflict', as he called it, caused by a voltaic current, deflected a magnetic needle, to Maxwell's momentous sentence 'that light consists in the transverse undulations of the same medium which is the cause of electric and magnetic phenomena'.

However, each significant new synthesis exacts a price. The matrices which enter into it are not simply coupled together; they must be integrated, and in the process of integration become modified in various ways and to various degrees. By and large, only technical innovations and minor discoveries result from a simple additive process which leaves the components intact—neither the Möbius loop nor the principles of electric resistance were the worse off after their union. But when Einstein bisociated space and time, both took on a bewilderingly new look in the process; and so did energy and matter. The progress of science, like an ancient desert trail, is strewn with the bleached skeletons of discarded theories, doctrines, and axioms which seemed to possess eternal life. The dramatic mergers of the last century entailed the sacrifice of beliefs which had constituted the very backbone of their separate disciplines—phlogistons, calorifics, 'vital fluids', and luminiferous ether, the electric and magnetic effluvia.

Thus every revolution has a destructive aspect. But the destructions wrought by the nineteenth century had a quasi-Victorian modesty compared to the twentieth. Within the lifetime of our generation we have seen matter evaporate, causality shaken, parity dethroned, infinity put into its place (wherever that may be); above all, we were given a new version of the Second Commandment: 'Thou shalt not make unto thee any graven image or model of anything that is in the Heavens above or that is in the Atoms beneath.'

Thus, on the positive side we have a series of confluences, as in a vast river system, of the different 'effluvia' into the unitary concept of energy, of the ninety-odd chemical elements into the same sub-atomic building blocks; and finally, energy and mass, particle and wave are all swallowed up in the majestic river delta; while on the destructive side we have an equally impressive series of floods and devastating erosions. For it is in the nature of the bisociative process that the impact of the two matrices makes each of them appear in a new light, so that axioms which had been taken for granted, and hidden assumptions built into their texture, stand mercilessly revealed. One such axiom, that everything that moves must have a mover, survived for two thousand years. Another, that we are entitled to extrapolate our conception of reality towards the infinitely large and the infinitely small, has collapsed only recently. And Einstein's 'God does not play dice with the world', which dates back to the Old Testament, is still *sub judice*. The destructive effects of scientific revolutions also display a hierarchic order: the closer they get to the basic axioms of thought, the more agonising the reappraisal which they demand.

Now science is made by scientists, and thus the destructive aspect of scientific revolutions must reflect some element of destructiveness in the scientific mind; or, to put it more politely, a preparedness to go recklessly against accepted beliefs. This destructive-constructive mentality I would suggest as the fourth criterion of creativity. It is related to originality, but should not be confused with it—the invention of the zip-fastener was highly original but not destructive. It is also related to the third criterion which remains to be briefly discussed: the intervention of extra-conscious processes, commonly called hunches.

The safest assumption is that hunches, like babies, are brought by the stork. One could fill a whole dictionary with quotations, from Pythagoras to Einstein, all of them testifying to hunches of unknown, extra-conscious origin. However, the concept of unconscious mentation loses both its mystical halo and its clinical odour if we avoid the Cartesian fallacy of equating mental activities with conscious thinking; and recognise instead that awareness of one's own activities is a matter of degree, of a continuous gradient, reaching from the unconsciousness of homeostatic regulations, to fringe-conscious perceptions, and up to the optimum condition of focal awareness. But that optimum condition is not always the most productive. 'Full consciousness is a narrow thing,' wrote Einstein; and he added that his creative thinking consisted of a kind of 'combinatorial play', the elements of which were vague, visual and kinesthetic images. It seems that pinpointing the task with the narrow beam of focal awareness is indispensable at certain times and stages of mental work, but in other situations it can become an impediment.

Such situations arise when the problem cannot be solved by any conventional rule of the game and requires some far-fetched, reckless combination of ideas which seems unacceptable to the sober, disciplined mind. The true scientist, like the true artist, is an uneasy mixture of the adventurer and the pedant. A Chinese proverb says that there is a time for fishing and a time for drying the nets; and there are times when the adventurer imprisoned in the pedant cries to be let out to go fishing. The disciplined routines of thought within the framework of a single conventional matrix are the vehicles of scientific progress at normal times; but at times of crisis, caused by the appearance of new data or a new type of question, matrices which have outlived their usefulness can become straitjackets. To unlearn is more difficult than to learn; and it seems that the agonising task of breaking up rigid cognitive structures and reassembling them into a new synthesis cannot always be performed in the full daylight of the conscious rational mind. It is more often done by reverting to those more fluid, less committed forms of mentation which normally operate in the twilight outside the beam of focal awareness or on a less specialised level of the mental hierarchy. These interventions of extra-conscious processes in the creative act range from the trivial to the dramatic, from James Watt's kettle to Kekulé's dream; but there is a vast literature on the subject and there is no need to go into it.

If you take a kind of grandstand view of the history of any branch of science, you will find a rhythmic alternation between long periods of relatively peaceful evolution and shorter bursts of revolutionary change. Only in the peaceful periods which follow after a major break-through is the progress of science continuous and cumulative in the strict sense. It is a period of consolidating the newly conquered frontiers, of verifying, assimilating, elaborating and extending the new synthesis: a time for drying the nets. It may last a few years or several generations; but sooner or later the emergence of new empirical data, of new developments in some adjacent branch of knowledge, or a change in the philosophical climate, leads to a hardening of the matrix into a closed system, a defensive attitude, the rise of a new orthodoxy. This produces a crisis, a period of fertile anarchy in which rival theories proliferate—until the new synthesis is achieved and the cycle starts again; but this time perhaps aiming in a different direction, along different parameters, asking a different kind of question.

This brings us back to the axiom that science is made by scientists, and not the other way round. The historic cycle which I have just described could be regarded as a magnified projection of the various stages in the process of individual discovery according to the classic schema by Helmholtz and Graham Wallas: conscious preparation; incubation; illumination; verification and consolidation. On the historic plane the last stage of one cycle shades into the first stage of the next. The period of 'fertile anarchy' which characterises the crisis corresponds to the feverish combinatorial games in the period of incubation; lastly, illumination—the emergence of the new synthesis—is mostly brought about by a quick succession of individual discoveries, often including multiple discoveries.

One could also call the revolutionary phases the romantic, and the peaceable phases the classical periods in the history of science. The former appeal to the reckless adventurer, the latter to the pedantic stickler in the Janus-faced scientist. This split personality seems to me both the glory and the predicament of the trade. Its glory, because at best it combines flights of imagination with meticulous respect for fact;

having one's head in the clouds and one's feet solidly planted in the mud. Its predicament, because either face can also turn into an ugly grimace—that of the obsessive crank's, or of blinkered orthodoxy. This explains perhaps why so many histories of science are written either as a chronicle of heroic exploits, or as a chronicle of scandals. Recently the second style has come into fashion; and indeed there is hardly a period or branch in the history of science without its scandals, martyrs, and skeletons rattling in cupboards. No less a man than Max Planck wrote from bitter experience:

> a new scientific truth does not triumph by convincing its opponents and making them see the light, but rather because its opponents eventually die, and a new generation grows up that is familiar with it.[4]

But, exaggeration apart, we also know the other side of the picture—that without the necessary scepticism, conservatism, and emotional commitment to the prevailing theories and rules of the game, the whole scientific enterprise would go to pieces. Michael Polanyi has given us a profound analysis of this unavoidable subjectivity and emotionalism in the scientist's attitude.[5]

I have suggested four criteria of creativity: originality, the improbability of the combination, its constructive-destructive aspect, and the intervention of extra-conscious factors. There is no need to dwell further on those other factors which provide the counterweight, the necessary ballast for the creative adventure. Nor, I trust, is it necessary to stress the obvious fact that virtually everything I have said about the mentality of the scientist also applies *mutatis mutandis* to his stepbrother, the artist.

Let me switch for the last time from the individual scientist to science as a collective enterprise. The overall view of evolutionary and revolutionary cycles which I have suggested in two earlier works has certain affinities with the views which Thomas Kuhn has independently arrived at in his book, *The Structure of Scientific Revolutions*, where he calls the peaceful periods 'normal science' and describes revolution as 'paradigm changes'. This is an approach rather different from George Sarton's well-known theory which holds that the history of science is the only history which displays a cumulative progress of knowledge, and that accordingly the progress of science is the only yardstick by which we can measure the progress of mankind.

Perhaps so—provided that we realise that the line of progress is not a curve approaching its asymptote, but a zigzag line; and that the yardstick is a relativistic yardstick. This does not mean, of course, that science does not advance; only that it advances in an unpredictable, jerky, erratic way. I have compared the great conceptual syntheses of the last hundred years to a river delta. But each confluence is also followed by a fanning out of specialised branches, subdividing into capillaries of more and more esoteric character. To change the metaphor: increasing specialisation is like the branching out of arteries; the sequence of mergers is like the reverse confluence of veins. The cycle which results makes the evolution of ideas appear as a tale of ever-repeated differentiations, specialisations, and reintegrations on a higher level of the hierarchy—a progression from primordial unity, through variety, to more complex patterns of unity in variety.

REFERENCES

1. Kuhn, T. (1962) *The Structure of Scientific Revolutions*, University of Chicago Press.
2. Polya, G. (1945) *How to Solve it*, Princeton University Press.
3. Hadamard, J. (1949) *The Psychology of Invention in the Mathematical Field*, Princeton University Press.
4. Planck, M. (1949) *Scientific Autobiography and Other Papers*, Philosophical Library, New York.
5. Polanyi, M. (1958) *Personal Knowledge*, Routledge and Kegan Paul.

Biological and Mental Evolution: an Exercise in Analogy

Substance of an address delivered at the Bicentennial
Celebration commemorating the birth of James Smithson, held at
the Smithsonian Institute in Washington, September 16–18, 1965. *

Allow me to take you on a ride on the treacherous wings of analogy, starting with an excursion into genetics. Creativity —the main subject of this paper—is a concept notoriously difficult to define; and it is sometimes useful to approach a difficult subject by way of contrast. The opposite of the creative individual is the pedant, the slave of habit, whose thinking and behaviour move in rigid grooves. His biological equivalent is the over-specialised animal. Take, for example, that charming and pathetic creature, the koala bear, which specialises in feeding on the leaves of a particular variety of eucalyptus tree and on nothing else; and which, in lieu of fingers, has hook-like claws, ideally suited for clinging to the bark of the tree—and for nothing else. Some of our departments of higher learning seem expressly designed for breeding koala bears.

* Published in *Knowledge Among Men, Eleven Essays on Science, Culture and Society*, New York, 1966.

Sir Julian Huxley has described over-specialisation as the principal cause why evolution in all branches of the animal kingdom—except man's—seems to have ended either in stagnation or in extinction. But, having made his point, he drew a conclusion which you may find less convincing. 'Evolution,' he concluded, 'is thus seen as an enormous number of blind alleys with a very occasional path to progress. It is like a maze in which almost all turnings are wrong turnings.'[1] With due respect, I think this metaphor is suspiciously close to the old-fashioned behaviourist's view of the rat in the maze as a paradigm of human learning. In both cases the explicit or tacit assumption is that progress results from a kind of blind man's buff—random mutations preserved by natural selection, or random tries preserved by reinforcement—and that that is all there is to it. However, it is possible to dissent from this view without invoking a *deus ex machina*, or a Socratic *daimon*, by making the simple assumption that, while random events no doubt play an important part in the picture, that is not all there is to it.

One line of escape from the maze is indicated by a phenomenon known to students of evolution by the ugly name of paedomorphosis, a term coined by Garstang[2] some forty years ago. The existence of the phenomenon is well established; but there is little mention of it in the text-books, perhaps because it runs against the *Zeitgeist*. It indicates that in certain circumstances evolution can re-trace its steps, as it were, along the path which led to the dead-end and make a fresh start in a more promising direction. To put it simply, paedomorphosis means the appearance of some evolutionary novelty in the *larval or embryonic* stage of the ancestral animal, a novelty which may disappear before the adult stage is reached, but which reappears in the *adult* descendant. This bit of evolutionary magic is made possible by the well-known mechanism of neoteny, that is to say, the gradual retardation of bodily development beyond the age of sexual maturity, with the result that breeding takes place while the animal still displays larval or juvenile features. Hardy,[3] de Beer[4] and others have pointed out that if this tendency toward 'prolonged childhood' were accompanied by a corresponding squeezing out of the later adult stages of ontogeny, the result would be a rejuvenation and de-specialisation of the race which would thus regain some of its lost adaptive plasticity. But of even greater importance than this re-winding of the biological clock is the fact that in the paedomorphic type of evolution selective pressure operates on the early, malleable stages of ontogeny. In contrast to this, gerontomorphosis— the appearance of novel characters in the late-adult stages— can only modify structures which are already highly specialised. One is accordingly led to expect that the major evolutionary advances were due to paedomorphosis and not to gerontomorphosis—to changes in the larval or embryonic, and not in the adult, stage.

Let me give an example, which will make clearer what I am driving at. There is now strong evidence in favour of the theory, proposed by Garstang[2] in 1922, that the chordates, and thus we, the vertebrates, descended from the larval state of some primitive echinoderm, perhaps rather like the sea-urchin or sea-cucumber. Now an adult sea-cucumber would not be a very inspiring ancestor—it is a sluggish creature which looks like an ill-stuffed sausage, lying on the sea-bottom. But its free-floating larva is a much more promising proposition: unlike the adult, it has bilateral symmetry, a ciliary band presumed to be the forerunner of the neural fold, and other sophisticated features not found in the adult animal. We must assume that the sedentary adult residing on the sea-bottom had to rely on mobile larvae to spread the species far and wide in the ocean, as plants scatter their seeds in the wind; that the larvae, which had to fend for themselves, exposed to much stronger selective pressures than the adults, gradually became more fish-like; and lastly became sexually mature while still in the free-swimming, larval state—thus giving rise to a new type of animal which never settled on the bottom at all and altogether eliminated the senile, sessile cucumber stage from its life-history.

It seems that the same re-tracing of steps to escape the dead-ends of the maze was repeated at each decisive evolutionary turning-point—the last time, so far as we know, when the line which bore our own species branched off from some ancestral primate. It is now generally recognised that the human adult resembles more the embryo of an ape than an adult ape. In both, the ratio of brain-weight to body-weight is disproportionately high; in both, the closing of the sutures of the skull is retarded to allow for further brain growth. The back to front axis through man's head—the direction of his line of sight—forms an angle of ninety degrees with his spinal column; a condition which, in apes and other mammals, is only found in the embryonic stage. The same applies to the angle between the uro-genital canal and the backbone, which accounts for the singularity of the human way of mating. Other embryonic—or, to use Bolk's[5] term, foetalised—features are the absence of brow-ridges, scantness of body-hair, retarded development of the teeth, and so on. As Haldane[6] has said: 'If human evolution is to continue along the same lines as in the past, it will probably involve a still greater prolongation of childhood and retardation of maturity. Some of the characters distinguishing adult man will be lost.' But there is a reverse to the medal, which Aldous Huxley gleefully showed us in *After Many a Summer*: artificial prolongation of the absolute life-span of man might provide an opportunity for features of the adult ape to re-appear in Methuselah. But this only by the way.

The essence of the process which I have described is a retreat from highly specialised adult forms of bodily structure and behaviour to an earlier, more plastic and less committed stage—followed by a sudden advance in a new direction. It is as if the stream of life had momentarily reversed its course, flowing uphill for a while, then opened up a new stream-bed —leaving the koala bear stranded on its tree like a discarded hypothesis. We have now reached the crucial point in our

264

excursion, because it seems to me that this process of *reculer pour mieux sauter*—of drawing back to leap, of undoing and re-doing—is a basic feature of all significant progress, both in biological and mental evolution.

It can be shown, I think, that these two types of progress —the emergence of biological novelties and the creation of mental novelties—are analogous processes on different levels of the developmental hierarchy. But to demonstrate the connection we must proceed stepwise from lower to higher organisms. One of the fundamental properties of living organisms is their power of *self-repair*, and the most dramatic manifestations of this power are the phenomena of regeneration (which Needham[7] called 'one of the more spectacular pieces of magic in the repertoire of living organisms'). Primitive creatures, like flatworms, when cut into slices, can regenerate a whole animal from a tiny fragment; Amphibia can regenerate limbs and organs; and once more the 'magic' is performed by *reculer pour mieux sauter*—the regression of specialised tissues to a genetically less committed, quasi-embryonic stage, a de-differentiation or de-specialisation followed by a re-differentiation.

Now the replacement of a lost limb or lost eye is a phenomenon of a quite different order from the adaptive processes in a normal environment. Regeneration could be called a meta-adaptation to traumatising challenges. The power to perform such meta-adaptations manifests itself only when the challenge exceeds a critical limit and can only be met by having recourse to the genetic plasticity of the embryonic stage. We have just seen that the major phylogenetic changes were brought about by a similar retreat from adult to embryonic forms. Indeed, the main line of development which led up to our species could be described as a series of operations of phylogenetic self-repair: of escapes from blind alleys by the undoing and re-moulding of maladapted structures.

Evidently, self-repair by the individual produces no evolutionary novelty, it merely restores the *status quo ante*.

265

But that is all the individual needs in order to regain its normal adaptive balance in a static environment (assuming that the traumatising disturbance was only a momentary one). Phylogenetic 'self-repair', on the other hand, implies changes in the genotype to restore the adaptive balance in a changing environment.

As we move toward the higher animals, the power of regenerating physical structures is superseded by the equally remarkable power of the nervous system to reorganise its mode of function. (Ultimately, of course, these reorganisations must also involve structural changes of a fine-grained nature in terms of circuitry, molecular chemistry or both, and so we are still moving along a continuous line.) Lashley[8] taught his rats certain visual discrimination skills; when he removed their optical cortex, the learning was gone, as one would expect; but, contrary to what one would expect, the mutilated rats were able to learn the same tasks again. Some other brain area, not normally specialising in visual learning, must have taken over this function, deputising for the lost area. Similar feats of meta-adaptation have been reported in insects, birds, chimpanzees and so on.

But let us get on to man, and to those lofty forms of self-repair which we call self-realisation, and which include creativity in its broadest sense. Psycho-therapy, ancient and modern, from shamanism down to contemporary forms of abreaction therapy, has always relied on what Ernst Kris[9] has called 'regression in the service of the ego'. The neurotic with his compulsions, phobias and elaborate defence-mechanisms is a victim of maladaptive specialisation—a koala bear hanging on for dear life to a barren telegraph pole. The therapist's aim is to regress the patient to an infantile or primitive condition; to make him retrace his steps to the point where they went wrong, and to come up again, metamorphosed, re-born. Goethe's *Stirb und Werde*, the inexhaustible variations of the archetype of death and resurrection, dark night and spiritual rebirth, all revolve around this basic paradigm—Joseph in the well, Jesus in the tomb, Buddha in the desert, Jonah in the belly of the whale.

There is no sharp dividing line between self-repair and self-realisation. All creative activity is a kind of do-it-yourself therapy, an attempt to come to terms with traumatising experiences. In the scientist's case the trauma is some apparent paradox of Nature, some anomaly in the motion of the planets, the sting of data which contradict each other, disrupt an established theory, and make nonsense of his cherished beliefs. In the artist's case, challenge and response are manifested in his tantalising struggle to express the inexpressible, to conquer the resistance of his medium, to escape from the distortions and restraints imposed by the conventional styles and techniques of his time.

In other words, the so-called revolutions in the history of both science and art are successful escapes from blind alleys. The evolution of science is neither continuous nor strictly cumulative except for those periods of consolidation and elaboration, which follow immediately after a major breakthrough. Sooner or later, however, the process of consolidation leads to increasing rigidity and orthodoxy, and so into the dead-end of over-specialisation. The proliferation of esoteric jargons which seems to characterise this phase reminds one sometimes of the monstrous antlers of the Irish elk, and sometimes of the neurotic's elaborate defence-mechanisms against the threats of reality. Eventually, the process leads to a crisis, and thus to a new revolutionary break-through—followed by another period of consolidation, a new orthodoxy, and so the cycle starts again.

In the history of art, this cyclic process is even more obvious: periods of cumulative progress within a given school and technique end inevitably in stagnation, mannerism or decadence, until the crisis is resolved by a revolutionary shift in sensibility, emphasis, style.

Every revolution has a destructive and a constructive aspect. In science the destruction is wrought by jettisoning previously unassailable doctrines, including some seemingly self-evident axioms of thought. In art, it involves an equally agonising re-appraisal of accepted values, criteria of relevance, frames of perception. When we discuss the evolution of art and science from the historian's detached point of view, this un-doing and re-doing process appears as a normal and inevitable part of the whole story. But when we focus our attention on any concrete individual who initiated a revolutionary change, we are immediately made to realise the immense intellectual and emotional obstacles he had to overcome I mean not only the inertial forces of society; the primary locus of resistance against heretical novelty is inside the skull of the individual who conceives of it. It reverberates in Kepler's agonised cry when he discovered that the planets move in elliptical pathways: 'who am I, Johannes Kepler, to destroy the divine symmetry of the circular orbits!'. On a more down-to-earth level the same agony is reflected in Jerome Bruner's[10] experimental subjects who, when shown for a split second a playing card with a black queen of hearts, saw it as red, as it should be; and when the card was shown again, reacted with nausea at such a perversion of the laws of Nature. To unlearn is more difficult than to learn; and it seems that the task of breaking up rigid cognitive structures and reassembling them into a new synthesis cannot, as a rule, be performed in the full daylight of the conscious, rational mind. It can only be done by reverting to those more fluid, less committed and specialised forms of ideation which normally operate in the twilight below the level of focal awareness. Such intervention of unconscious processes in the creative act is now generally, if sometimes reluctantly, accepted even by behaviourists with a strong positivist bias. Allow me, therefore, to take it for granted that in the period of incubation—to use Graham Wallas's[11] term—the creative individual experiences a temporary regression to patterns of thinking which are normally inhibited in the rational adult.

But it would be a great over-simplification to identify— as is sometimes done—these patterns with Freud's so-called 'Primary Process'. The primary process is supposedly devoid of logic, governed by the pleasure principle, apt to confuse perception and hallucination, expressed in spontaneous action, and accompanied by massive affective discharge. I believe that between this very primary process, and the so-called secondary process governed by the reality principle, we must interpolate a whole hierarchy of cognitive structures which are not simply mixtures of primary and secondary processes, but are autonomous systems in their own right, each governed by a distinct set of rules. The paranoid delusion, the dream, the daydream, free association, the mentality of children at various ages and of primitives at various stages, should not be lumped together, for each has its own logic or rules of the game. But while clearly different in many respects, all these forms of ideation have certain features in common, since they are ontogenetically, and perhaps phylogenetically, older than those of the civilised adult. I have elsewhere[12] called them 'games of the underground', because if not kept under restraint they would disrupt the routines of disciplined thinking. But when disciplined thinking is at the end of its tether, a temporary indulgence in these underground games may suddenly produce a solution which was beyond the reach of the conscious, rational mind. I have discussed this process in some detail in a recent book[12] and shall not dwell on it. The point I want to make here is that the creation of novelty in mental evolution follows the same pattern of *reculer pour mieux sauter*, of a temporary regression to a naive or juvenile level, followed by a forward leap, which we have found in biological evolution. We can carry the analogy further and interpret the Aha reaction, or 'Eureka!' cry, as the signal of a happy escape from a blind alley—an act of mental self-repair, achieved by the de-differentiation of cognitive structures to a more plastic state, and the resulting liberation of creative potentials—the equivalent of the release of genetic growth-potentials in regenerating tissues.

It is a truism to say that in mental evolution social inheritance replaces genetic inheritance. But there is a less trivial parallel between phylogenesis and the evolution of ideas: neither of them proceeds along a continuous curve in a strictly cumulative manner. Newton said that if he saw farther than others it was because he stood on the shoulders of giants. But did he really stand on their shoulders or some other part of their anatomy? He adopted Galileo's laws of free fall, but rejected Galileo's astronomy. He adopted Kepler's planetary laws, but demolished the rest of the Keplerian edifice. He did not take as his point of departure their completed 'adult' theories, but retraced their development to the point where it had gone wrong. Nor was the Keplerian edifice built on top of the Copernican structure. That ramshackle structure of epicycles he tore down and kept only its foundations. Nor did Copernicus continue to build where Ptolemy had left off. He went back two thousand years to Aristarchus. The great revolutionary turns in the evolution of ideas have a decidedly paedomorphic character. The new paradigm, to use Thomas Kuhn's[13] term, which emerges from the revolution is not derived from a previous adult paradigm; not from the aged sea-urchin but from its mobile larva, floating in the currents of the ocean. Only in the relatively peaceful periods of consolidation and elaboration do we find gerontomorphosis—small improvements to a fully mature body of knowledge. In the history of art the process is again all too obvious; there is no need to elaborate on it.

I began with a wistful remark about the treacherous wings of analogy, aware of the fact that those who trust these waxen wings usually share the fate of Icarus. But it is one thing to argue from analogy, and quite another to point to an apparent similarity which has perhaps not been paid sufficient attention, and then to ask whether that similarity has some significance or whether it is trivial and deceptive. I believe that the parallel between certain processes underlying biological and mental evolution has some significance. Biological evolution could be described as a history of escapes from over-specialisation, the evolution of ideas as a series of escapes from the bondage of mental habit; and the escape mechanism in both cases is based on the same principles. We get an inkling of them through the phenomena of regeneration—the remoulding of structures and reorganisation of functions—which only enter into action when the challenge exceeds a critical limit. They point to the existence of unsuspected 'meta-adaptive' potentials which are inhibited or dormant in the normal routines of existence, and, when revealed, make us sometimes feel that we move like sleepwalkers in a world of untapped resources and unexplored possibilities.

It could be objected that I have presented a reductionist view; that it is sacrilegious to call the creation of a Brahms symphony or of Maxwell's field equations an act of self-repair, and to compare it with the mutation of a sea-squirt larva, the regeneration of a newt-tail, the relearning process in the rat or the rehabilitation of patients by psycho-therapy. But I think that such a view is the opposite of sacrilegious. It points, however tentatively, at a common denominator, a factor of purposiveness, without invoking a *deus ex machina*. It does not deny that trial and error are inherent in all progressive development. But there is a world of difference between the random tries of the monkey at the typewriter, and the process which I called, for lack of a better name, *reculer pour mieux sauter*. The first means reeling off all possible responses in the organism's repertory until the correct one is hit on by chance and stamped in by reinforcement. The second may still be called trial and error, but of a purposive kind, using more complex, sophisticated methods: a groping and searching, retreating and advancing towards a goal. 'Purpose,' to quote Herbert J. Muller,[14] 'is not imported into Nature and need not be puzzled over as a strange or divine something. . . . It is simply implicit in the fact or organisation.' This directiveness of vital processes is present all along the line, from conscious behaviour down to what Needham[7] called 'the striving of the blastula to grow into a chicken'. How tenacious and resourceful that striving is has been demonstrated by experimental embryology, from Speeman to Paul Weiss—though its lessons have not yet been fully digested.

Thus to talk of goal-directedness or purpose in ontogeny has become respectable again. In phylogeny the monkey still seems to be hammering away at the typewriter, perhaps because the crude alternatives that had been offered— amorphous entelechies, or the Lysenko brand of Lamarckism —were even more repellent to the scientific mind. On the other hand, in recent years the rigid, atomistic concepts of Mendelian genetics have undergone a softening process and have been supplemented by a whole series of new terms with an almost holistic ring. Thus we learn that the genetic system represents a 'micro-hierarchy' which exercises its selective and regulative control on the molecular, chromo-somal and cellular level; that development is 'canalised', stabilised by 'developmental homeostasis' or 'evolutionary homoestasis'[15] so that mutations affect not a single unit character but a 'whole organ in a harmonious way',[16] and, finally, that these various forms of 'internal selection' create a restricted 'mutation spectrum'[17] or may even have a 'direct, moulding influence guiding evolutionary change along certain avenues'[18]—and all this happens long before external, Darwinian selection gets to work. But if this is the case, then the part played by a lucky chance mutation is reduced to that of the trigger which releases the co-ordinated action of the system; and to maintain that evolution is the product of blind chance means to confuse the simple action of the trigger, governed by the laws of statistics, with the complex, purposive processes which it sets off. Their pur-posiveness is manifested in different ways on different levels of the hierarchy, from the self-regulating properties of the genetic system through internal and external selection, cul-minating perhaps in the phenomena of phylogenetic self-repair: escapes from blind alleys and departures in new directions. On each level there is trial and error, but on each level it takes a more sophisticated form. Some twenty years

272

ago, Tolman and Krechevsky[19] created a stir by proclaiming that the rat learns to run a maze by forming hypotheses; soon it may be permissible to extend the metaphor and to say that evolution progresses by making and discarding hypotheses.

Any directive process, whether you call it selective, adaptive or expectative, implies a reference to the future. The equifinality of developmental processes, the striving of the blastula to grow into an embryo, regardless of the obstacles and hazards to which it is exposed, might lead the unprejudiced observer to the conclusion that the pull of the future is as real and sometimes more important than the pressure of the past. The pressure may be compared to the action of a compressed spring, the pull to that of an extended spring, threaded on the axis of time. Neither of them is more or less mechanistic than the other. If the future is completely determined in the Laplacian sense, then there is nothing to choose between the actions of the two springs. If it is indeterminate in the Heisenbergian sense, then indeterminacy works in both directions, and the distant past is as blurred and unknowable as the future; and if there is something like a free choice operating within the air-bubbles in the stream of causality, then it must be directed towards the future and oriented by feed-back from the past.

REFERENCES

1. Huxley, J. *Man in the Modern World*, 13, London and New York, 1948.
2. Garstang, W. *J. Linnean Soc. Lond. (Zoology)*, **35**, 81, 1922.
3. Hardy, A. C. in *Evolution as a Process* London and New York, 1954.
4. de Beer, G. R. *Embryos and Ancestors*, Oxford, 1940.
5. Bolk, L. *Das Problem der Menschwerdung*, Jena, 1926.
6. Haldane, J. B. S. *The Causes of Evolution*, 150, London, 1932.
7. Needham, A. E. *New Scientist*, London, November 2, 1961.

8. Lashley, K. S. *Brain Mechanisms and Intelligence*, Chicago, 1929.
9. Kris, E. *Psychoanalytic Explorations in Art*, New York, 1952.
10. Bruner, J. S. and Postman, L. *J. of Personality*, XVIII, 1949.
11. Wallas, G. *The Art of Thought*, London, 1954.
12. Koestler, A. *The Act of Creation*, London and New York, 1964.
13. Kuhn, T. H. *The Structure of Scientific Revolutions*, Chicago, 1962.
14. Muller, H. J. *Science and Criticism*, New Haven, Conn., 1943.
15. Cannon, H. G. *The Evolution of Living Things*, Manchester, 1958.
16. Waddington, C. H. *The Listener*, London, November 13, 1952.
17. Spurway, H. in *Supplemento. La Ricerca Scientifica*, Pallanza Symp., **18**, Cons. Naz. delle Richerche, Rome, 1949.
18. For a survey of literature in this field see Whyte, L. L. *Internal Factors in Evolution*, London, 1965.
19. Krechevsky, L. *Psychol. Rev.*, **39**, 1932.

Polemics and Rejoinders

To Covet a Swallow

The article on 'A Love Affair with Norway', as originally printed in *The Observer*, ended with a Postscript which read:

> Though Goeteborg is not in Norway but across the frontier in Sweden, I may be forgiven for including a piece of incidental information which I discovered there. While sightseeing in Goeteborg, I noticed a memorial tablet on a house overlooking the canal, which said that the Czech composer, Friedrich Smetana, had lived there (in 1860, if I remember rightly) while composing his symphonic poem, *The Moldava*. This stuck in my memory, because it is a well-known fact that the Israeli National Anthem is a variation on a theme in that symphony.
>
> I inquired what Smetana had been doing in Goeteborg, and was told that he had been invited to conduct the orchestra of the Philharmonic Society, that he became interested in Swedish folk music, and stayed nearly ten years in the country. As for that famous theme in the Moldava Symphony, whose Slavonic melancholy captivated the hearts of Israel, it is the transposition from a major into a minor key of an old Swedish regional folk-song, 'Ach Wärmeland du sköna'—O you beautiful Wärmeland.
>
> Thus the Hebrew anthem praising the beauties of the River Jordan is derived from Smetana's symphony in praise of the River Moldava, which is derived from a Swedish song in praise of the province of Wärmeland, home of the Gösta Berling Saga. All of which goes to prove the smallness of this world, and its free trade in emotions.

This incidental piece of information had a curious aftermath. A gentleman attached to the Embassy of the Czechoslovak People's Republic wrote an angry letter to *The Observer*, denying that Smetana adopted a foreign tune for the Moldava—which, he said, 'is based, like so many of the themes of this most patriotic of all Czech composers, on the popular folk melodies sung by the Czech people'.

Another correspondent, however (Mr. Eric Conrad), arrived at the opposite conclusion. 'The fact is,' he wrote, '—and I have always thought it both a puzzling and an exciting one—that several nations in Europe share (in slightly varied forms) the simple little tune to which Smetana's melody and the Israeli anthem can easily be reduced. In England it is a favourite nursery rhyme ("Baa-baa Black Sheep"), in France it is also a nursery rhyme (*Ah vous dirai-je, Maman*). You will easily recognise that these tunes . . . form the skeleton on which Smetana's more elaborate tune is (no doubt unconsciously) built.'

After this cosmopolitan broadside, the gentleman from the Czechoslovak People's Republic wrote a second letter to *The Observer*, remembering that there is 'a well-known Czech nursery rhyme *Kočka leze dirou*, "a cat crawls through a hole,"' which Smetana knew, and 'which is almost identical' with his theme.

Thoroughly bewildered by these disclosures about the Israeli anthem's unsuspected origins, I appealed for expert advice. My prayers were answered by Thurston Dart, then of Cambridge University, whose conclusions outline, in a charming manner, the moral of this little episode (*The Observer*, 20.7.1960):

> A folk-tune is like a migrant bird; the fact that it is observed in a given place at a given time cannot be taken as proof that it originated there. A century ago Smetana may have encountered the beautiful theme of his symphony either in Goeteborg or in Bohemia, but the folk-song ornithologist knows of its currency long before that.

The theme was first written down soon after 1600, in a

manuscript now in a private collection in Florence. There it is described as the song 'Fuggi, fuggi', composed by Giuseppino. Though little is known about him, contemporary references show that he was a tenor singer. He belonged to the class of extemporising musician-poets best represented today by the calypso singers of the West Indies, and his numerous villanelles in the Neapolitan style were immensely popular among all classes of society.

'Fuggi, fuggi' is one of these Neapolitan villanelles, and during the seventeenth century its flight may be traced over a great part of Europe . . . 'Baa-baa Black Sheep' and *Ah vous dirai-je Maman* are boiled down, corrupted versions of the original tune.

It seems to me, therefore, that neither Sweden, Czechoslovakia, France, England nor Israel can have much right to claim Smetana's theme. To covet a folk-song is as silly and undignified as to covet a swallow, anyway, but the music historian's evidence should perhaps be heard. According to him, the tune was hatched in Italy, two centuries and more before Smetana was born; by the end of the seventeenth century it had flown over most international frontiers of its time, free and unchallenged.

'Darkness at Noon'
and 'The Strangled Cry'

In the 'University Lectures' series, broadcast by Radio Free Europe in 1962, the Polish emigré writer, K. A. Jelenski, commented as follows on the Moscow show trials of the nineteen-thirties:

> Many people in the west could not bring themselves to believe that men of sound mind could confess to crimes they had never committed. We owe it to Koestler's *Darkness at Noon* that the dialectics of the Russian purges were finally understood. Today we also know that, by stressing one of the most interesting aspects of the Moscow confessions, and the one most difficult to understand for non-Communists—the renunciation of life itself as a last service to the Party—Koestler conferred on these confessions a sinister dignity which they did not altogether possess. We know from Mr. Khrushchev that in this, as in so many other ways, Stalin's methods were entirely old-fashioned. Torture and the bait of peaceful dachas were the things that induced his victims to incriminate themselves.*

Later in the same broadcast series I was interviewed by its editor, George Urban. He took up Jelenski's point and thus gave me an opportunity to answer a criticism frequently heard in the days after Khrushchev's revelations.

* K. A. Jelenski, 'Varieties of Disenchantment', published in *Scaling the Wall—The Best of Radio Free Europe*, ed. G. R. Urban (Detroit, 1964).

280

URBAN   Since Khrushchev made his famous speeches at the 20th and 22nd Party Congresses revealing the unpleasant things Stalin did to his opponents, I have seen it repeatedly said by quite knowledgeable people that your picture in *Darkness at Noon* of the way in which confessions were obtained by the police under Stalin was far-fetched . . . I would myself agree with K. A. Jelenski, who says in one of his writings that you 'conferred on these confessions a sinister dignity which they did not altogether possess'.

KOESTLER   In my novel there are several characters in prison—there is Rubashov, there is Harelip, there is a peasant from Siberia and there are others. Now Harelip is badly tortured, and the peasant from Siberia is also beaten. With Rubashov it is touch and go whether his investigators are going to put him to physical torture or wear his resistance down and argue him into capitulation. You see, human memory is a very faulty instrument. We all like to simplify, and remembering a story or a book such as *Darkness at Noon* a lot of people retain in their minds only one or two outstanding features. It is the most striking thing that sticks and the rest is forgotten. I never said that *everybody* confessed to do the Party a last service. I said that *a very few*, the hard core, confessed in this manner. Now why is this important?

Mainly because, I believe—even if you might think this somewhat sentimental—that the old Bolshevik guard, the Bukharins, the Zinovievs and Piatakovs, were great men, and it would be the final injustice to misinterpret the motives for which they died. It is not true that they succumbed to the promise of dachas or indicted themselves because they were tortured. They died for reasons which were human reason running amuck but within the logic of their own faith, and this is extremely important because intellectual murder is still going on in China; brainwashing was successfully practised on American soldiers during the Korean war, and a variant of the psychological technique which was used on the old Bolsheviks is now used on the people of China. It is easy to underestimate the subtlety of these methods—particularly if you compare them with the Nazi methods—because the Communists apply a mixture: they appeal to the weakness of the flesh and to the noblest things man possesses, his sense of duty and self-sacrifice.

As to my evidence concerning the 'hard core' of Bolsheviks on whom these methods were used, let me say this: first, I know at least three people who spoke from personal experience: they told me how they were not allowed to sleep because their interrogators wanted to catch them with their defences down, how then they were treated with great consideration and addressed as comrades, all this leading to the final demand—'there is a small thing the Party is asking of you', etc.

Then, of course, there is the evidence of others who had escaped from Soviet prisons. Now, one of these, whose story shows a clear likeness to my interrogation scenes, was not known to me until after my book was finished. The man I have in mind is General Krivitsky, whose report is, no doubt, the most authoritative. Krivitsky was head of the Fourth Bureau of the Red Army, that is of military intelligence for Western Europe, until in 1937 he broke with the regime. Twice the G.P.U. made an attempt to assassinate him in France, and a third time in the United States. The last was successful and it was made to appear as suicide. In December 1939, at a time when I had already finished all but the last chapter of *Darkness at Noon*, Krivitsky published his book *I Was Stalin's Agent*. I read the book only years later because, having got *Darkness at Noon* out of my system, I became allergic to the whole subject.

URBAN   Krivitsky's account of the method by which one of the accused at the first show trial was induced to confess comes so close to Rubashov's interrogation by Gletkin that I, for one, would regard it as the most telling evidence of the accuracy of the whole analysis you have given in *Darkness at Noon*. For here we have a writer who knows the internal logic in which the Communist mind works, particularly in this kind of dramatic confrontation. Here we have a conversation which is fiction, but then along comes a report from the files of the secret police and it proves to be almost identical with the kind of battle of wits and willpower you depicted for the reader between these two parties. I think this is the most striking thing about *Darkness at Noon*.

KOESTLER   I have discussed this all in detail in an auto-biographical book, *The Invisible Writing*. But, you know, there was no clairvoyance involved, and it is less striking than you think, because, although the police methods under Stalin were varied and subtle, there was a pattern to them. I had the help and evidence of personal friends who escaped by an extraordinary stroke of luck. They had been put through the whole works and I got a great many details from them. Of course, these were completely different cases from the one I tried to describe, but I could see the pattern. Also, if you have lived inside the Party you know the dialectic and you can re-enact for yourself the whole picture.

Today, Khrushchev says that the confessions were extorted by old-fashioned torture and bribery. But don't forget that, for all their denunciations of Stalin, the Soviet leaders have no interest in disclosing these methods. They have worked out a number of approaches which they think they can use on various people in various circumstances. The Secret Police is still there—why should it tell the world how hardy old Bolsheviks were brought to their knees?*

A quite different and rather unexpected criticism came from my old friend John Strachey.

In the eighteen months since its serial publication in *Encounter*, *The Strangled Cry* has come to be recognised as perhaps the most important thing which John Strachey has written. The issues

* Extract from broadcast discussion, September 1962, published in *Scaling the Wall* (see previous footnote).

of the magazine in which it appeared were quickly exhausted
... In form the essay is a study of the work of Koestler, Orwell,
Whittaker Chambers and Pasternak. In fact it is a highly
personal and deeply felt reflection on those basic issues—
political, moral, aesthetic and religious—which have wracked
the generation of European intellectuals of which Mr. Strachey
is a member.

This is how the publishers described John Strachey's last
work.* I have no doubt that it was his best book—regardless
of the fact that he accused me in it, tongue in cheek, of having
started 'the literature of reaction'. We had been close friends
from the late 'thirties—when we were both Communists—
until his sudden death in 1963. Thus our last divergence of
opinions could never be thrashed out. The point of his
accusation was that the 'literature of disenchantment'
(exemplified, in his view, by the works of Orwell, Chambers,
Pasternak and myself), 'is not only, and in the end not even
principally, a reaction against the values of present-day
Communism; it is also a reaction against five hundred years
of rationalism and empiricism; against, in short, the Enlightenment. That is its scandal and its power.' Strachey then
singled me out as the earliest sinner. He had first read *Darkness at Noon* in 1942, with considerable reluctance, as he
explains, because at that time his break with Communism
was as yet incomplete:

> It might have been supposed that I should have been, at
> that time, in a receptive mood ... But it was not so; I still had
> strong inhibitions to reading this kind of book about Russia ...
> I had nerved myself to read the book. Though I had not liked it,
> it had made a stunning impression. At that time only one thing
> about the book mattered: was it true? Were things in Russia
> really like this?
>
> But eighteen years do strange things to a book. To re-read
> *Darkness at Noon* today is to appreciate the seismic change in all
> our points of view. Nobody can today be in the least interested
> in whether the book is true or not: of course it is true. The

* *The Strangled Cry* (London, 1962).

murders, the tortures, the confessions, the starvation, all happened. Khrushchev has described them more authoritatively than Koestler. When it was published about twenty years ago, the book caused riots in Paris, broke friendships, split families, and was denounced by many people who were by no means Communists. Today no one is likely to feel particularly strongly about it. As an accusation the book has become beside the point. If it is to survive it must be for other qualities.

What then is left of Koestler's book, now that its main assertion has become a commonplace? A good deal is left as a matter of fact. This was the first book to begin to reveal the far-reaching consequences upon the mind and spirit of the West of the rejection of Communism. It revealed that Communism could not be rejected without . . . calling in question the whole rationalist tradition. The values which the book began to preach were subversive of much more than Communism . . . *Darkness at Noon* is the starting point of the literature of reaction . . . the retreat from rationalism.

John Strachey was still alive at the time of my broadcast discussion with George Urban:

URBAN In *The Strangled Cry* John Strachey makes the charge—and I have seen similar questions raised by others—that *Darkness at Noon* and much of the literature of disenchantment represent a retreat from rationalism . . . Do you think that your own books or Silone's thinking really represent a retreat from reason . . .?

KOESTLER It seems to me that John Strachey identifies 'reason' with the materialistic and mechanistic philosophies of the last century. Now these, of course, are as dead as mutton. Reason can be spoken of in many contexts. But whether you think of it in the ordinary sense as the power of thinking in orderly and sensible ways or, as some philosophers do, as a kind of universal goodness and intelligence, I think the 'literature of disenchantment' retreats from neither of these. What is has rejected is the arrogant and shallow optimism of the nineteenth century, and particularly the utilitarian

285

ethics of the nineteenth century. Utilitarianism and prag-
matism were the real targets of our protests. To think, as
Bentham did, that the worth of human action is determined
by its utility or expediency, is to open the way to the suffering
of countless millions. Silone, too, rebelled against these
ethically neutral ethics. Our 'strangled' cry was simply
uttered against the idea that ends justify means. The history
of the Soviet Union and of China have shown us that the
ends have a way of being more and more difficult to keep in
sight while the means perpetuate the evils which these ever-
receding ends are claimed to make acceptable and respectable . . . So I think it would be quite unfair to accuse us,
ex-Communists, of becoming figures out of Dostoyevsky's
novels, singing Gregorian hymns into our beards.

Urban also repeated another objection of John Strachey's:
that the arguments of Gletkin, the G.P.U. interrogator in the
novel, are 'so convincingly put that some people have been
influenced by them in a pro-Communist direction'. To this I
replied that evidently in a novel, as opposed to a propaganda
pamphlet, 'every character must be right and consistent
within its own logic. If for some readers the Gletkin passages
appear to be unduly convincing, I can only plead that the
Gletkins are terrifyingly convincing when you meet them
behind the prison walls of the Ljubljanka.'
By the time this appeared in print, John Strachey was
dead. I have never felt so sad having the last word.

Between the Lotus and the Robot

In August and October 1960, *Encounter* magazine printed two chapters from the book I was preparing after a prolonged stay in India and Japan, *The Lotus and the Robot* (published in 1961). The first, 'Yoga Unexpurgated', was a survey of contemporary Yoga practices in India, the second, 'A Stink of Zen', of contemporary Zen practices in Japan and America. Among those who participated in the ensuing controversy were the late Professor C. G. Jung, Mr. Christmas Humphreys, a prominent English practitioner of Zen Buddhism, and Professor G. Scholem of the University of Jerusalem.

Jung's long letter is included as a Postscript in the French and German translations of the book (it came too late for the English edition); it was one of his last appearances in print. The key passage said: 'In the main I fully agree with Koestler's rather unfavourable opinion [of contemporary Zen and Yoga practices]. His is a meritorious as well as a needful act of debunking, for which he deserves our gratitude. The picture he is drawing of Yoga and Zen is, as the view of the Western mind, rational, distant, and—as it were—unprejudiced and correct.'

Professor Scholem came up with a startling disclosure concerning one of the foremost prophets of the Zen cult in the West, which should be preserved for the record:

ZEN-NAZISM?

With reference to the article by Arthur Koestler, 'A Stink of Zen', in your October issue, I think I ought to make a remark illustrating his point concerning the amoralism of Zen teaching. Koestler goes in for a lengthy criticism of Eugen Herrigel's *Zen in the Art of Archery* and some other texts by Zen adherents. About one he says that what he quoted could 'come from a philosophically-minded Nazi journalist'. It has obviously escaped Koestler's attention that Eugen Herrigel, who wrote this widely discussed treatise, had in fact become a member of the Nazi Party after his return from Japan and having obtained whatever Zen illumination he might have got there. This fact has been carefully hushed up by the circle of his admirers after the war and it is thus small wonder that Koestler did not hear about it. Herrigel joined the Nazi Party after the outbreak of the war and some of his former friends in Frankfurt, who broke with him over this issue, told me in 1946 about his career as a convinced Nazi. He was known to have stuck it out to the bitter end. This was not mentioned in some biographical notes on Herrigel published by his widow, who built up his image as one concerned with the higher spiritual sphere only . . .

By an ironic coincidence, John Strachey's attack in *The Strangled Cry* was published by *Encounter* in the middle of the Zen dispute; this explains my rejoinder, winding up the controversy:

'In the November issue of *Encounter*, John Strachey accused me, rather flatteringly, of having started the "literature of reaction", the retreat from rationalism. In the December issue, Mr. Christmas Humphreys, Q.C., accused me of the opposite crime, of being too much of a rationalist to share in the "intuitive delights" of his particular brand of mysticism, i.e. Zen. I am not complaining; falling between two stools may be preferable to settling down, if both of them smell of dry rot.

'That Western rationalism has acquired that smell is evident, and tacitly agreed by all participants in this controversy. It seems equally obvious, and inevitable, that a culture threatened by strontium clouds should yearn for the Cloud of Unknowing. My point was that the simple abdication of reason in favour of a spurious mysticism does not resolve the dilemma; and I have tried to prove that both Yoga and Zen, *as practised today*, are spurious and degenerate. I am grateful to Professor Jung for his authoritative endorsement of this diagnosis, and not only for personal reasons; his statement will help to dispel the fog. With the remainder of his article, defending intuition against the monopolistic claims of logic, I am in full agreement; he apparently did not realise that this was the starting point of my book (and implied in its title, *The Lotus and the Robot*).

'Mr. Christmas Humphreys objected to my being only concerned with Zen in Japan and not in China. But Chinese Zen went into decline some five hundred years ago, and is virtually extinct; it is the Japanese brand, packaged for export by Professor Suzuki, that is dumped on the West. Then he quoted Suzuki himself to show that Zen should be tied *neither* to Japan *nor* to China, because it "has its own life independent of history". Now that statement is true of any system of ideas, but no longer true when that system becomes embodied in a church, cult, or school; and the only contemporary embodiment of Zen is Japanese Zen, as Mr. Humphreys well knows. So why quibble?

'And why must the Master and his pupils write book after book to explain that Zen cannot be explained, that it is "literally beyond thought, beyond the reach of thought, beyond the limits of the finest and most subtle thinking"—in a word, that it cannot be put into words? We know that not only mystical experience defies verbalisation; there is a whole range of intuitions, visual impressions, bodily sensations, which also refuse to be converted into verbal currency. Painters paint, dancers dance, musicians make music, instead of explaining that they are practising no-thought in their no-minds. Inarticulateness is not a monopoly of Zen; but it is the only school which made a philosophy out of it, whose exponents burst into verbal diarrhoea to prove constipation.

'In mediaeval Japan and earlier in China, Zen fulfilled a vital function as a deliberately amoral and illogical antidote to the rigours of a hierarchic, cramped, self-conscious society. Its motto was: reverse the paradox of the centipede, don't think, just walk. That's good advice to the centipede, but very bad in societies which tend to run amok. In the form in which it is taught and practised today, Zen spells intellectual and moral nihilism. The first, because the emphasis is not on marrying intuition to reason, but on castrating reason. And the second, because its moral detachment has degenerated into complacency towards, and complicity with, evil. As the Master himself tells us:

> 'Zen is . . . extremely flexible in adapting itself to almost any philosophy and moral doctrine as long as its intuitive teaching is not interfered with. It may be found wedded to anarchism or fascism, communism or democracy . . .*

'What is one to think of an "intuitive teaching" that can be "wedded" to the mystic of genocide? By virtue of its anti-rationality and amorality, Zen always held a fascination for a category of people in whom brutishness combines with pseudomysticism, from Samurai to Kamikaze to Beatnik. Mr. Humphreys is an exception; but the case of Herrigel (*Zen in the Art of Archery*), mentioned in Professor Scholem's letter, is typical. He was the star pupil among Western converts both before and after his Nazi career. In Dr. Suzuki's preface, written in 1953, to "this wonderful little book by a German philosopher", there is no mention of that past and no word of apology; instead the Master has the sweet gall to tell us how, through the practice of archery,

> 'the mind is brought into contact with the ultimate reality . . . "childlikeness" is restored after long years of training . . . When a man reaches that stage of spiritual development, he is a Zen artist of life . . . He is the showers, the ocean, the stars, the foliage.

'And the gas-chambers.

* *Zen and Japanese Culture*, by D. T. Suzuki (London, 1959), p. 63.

'When the archer had gone to Valhalla, Frau Gustie, his faithful and formidable widow, published a companion volume about *Zen in the Art of Flower Arrangement*, with another gushing preface by Dr. Suzuki in which reference was made to "the lilies of the field whose beauty was not surpassed by Solomon". It is time for the Professor to shut up and for the Western intelligentsia to recognise contemporary Zen as one of the sick jokes, slightly gangrened, which are always fashionable in ages of anxiety.

'Debunking is not an inspiring job. When John Donne wrote, "*T'is all in pieces, all cohesion gone*", he was uttering an earlier "strangled cry". He also wrote, "*With a strong sober thirst, my soule attends*"; and that thirst cannot be quenched by counterfeit spirits.'